THE AROMATIC CAT

An holistic approach to feline wellbeing,
using herbs, hydrosols, and essential oils.

Nayana Morag and
Julie-Anne Thorne

This book is intended as a guide for cat lovers and guardians who would like to use aromatic extracts in the routine management of health and well-being for their cat. It is not intended to replace regular veterinary care, nor is it intended to offer diagnosis, advice or treatment. Please consult with your veterinarian for diagnosis and possible treatment if you are concerned about your cat's health. The authors and publisher assume no liability in connection with use of the information presented in this book.

Published by:
OtE Press,Cp 7373
Sao Martinho das Amoreiras
7630-536
Portugal
First edition

Cover painting Rupa Bokhorst www.rupabokhorst.nl
Cover design Bogdan Matei
Interior design Bogdan Matei
All interior photographs property of Nayana Morag.

TABLE OF CONTENTS

Acknowledgements...7
Introduction...9
Good Foundations 11
The Aromatics..19
  Herbs 19
  Hydrosols...23
  Essential Oils..26
  Vegetable and Herbal Oils 29
How to Use Aromatics, Step by Step.........................33
What Can I Use Aromatics For?...............................49
How To Make Aromatic Lotions 59
Your Aromatic Pharmacy 63
Botanical Profiles..65
  Angelica Root 65
  Bergamot 68
  Carrot Seed 70
  Calendula 72
  Catnip..74
  Cedarwood Himalayan.....................................76
  Chamomile, German 78
  Chamomile, Roman..80
  Chickweed 82
  Clary Sage 84

Cistus 86
Comfrey 89
Fennel, Sweet 91
Frankincense 93
Geranium..95
Ginger...97
Helichrysum 99
Hemp..101
Hops 103
Jasmine 105
Juniper Berry...107
Lavender 109
Lemongrass 111
Linden Blossom 113
Lemon Balm 115
Neem 117
Neroli (Orange Blossom) 119
Nettle...121
Peppermint 123
Rose 125
Rosemary 127
St John's Wort 129
Sunflower Oil...131
Tea Tree...132
Thyme 134
Valerian Root...136
Vetiver 138
Violet Leaf 140
Yarrow 142
Ylang-Ylang...144
Clays and Powders 147

Clay 147
Diatomaceous Earth...148
Spirulina 149
Barley Grass 150
Aromatic Cross Reference Chart 151
Aromatics For Specific Conditions 155
Glossary of Terms 167
Index...173
Resources 179
Videos of Cats Interacting with Essential Oils 179
Books 180
Aromatic Suppliers...181
About Nayana...183
About Julie-Anne 185

ACKNOWLEDGEMENTS

From Nayana

Thank you to the many wonderful cats who have shared their love and wisdom with me through my life. Thank you to Julie-Anne for her most valuable contribution to bringing this book into being. Her passion for cat wellbeing is inspirational. Thanks to all of you who have supported my work with essential oils and animals over the years. And as always, thank you to my lovely partner, couldn't do it without you.

From Julie-Anne

I would like to thank Nayana for the opportunity to collaborate with her and to have our voices shared with the world through this book. My dear cat Pickle, who inspired me to create Naturally Cats and without whom I would not be helping the cats I am today. To you the readers, thank you for taking an interest in how to support your cat holistically. Finally, to all the cats who have taught me so much over the years, how to listen and to be their voice. This book is for you.

Naturally Cats

INTRODUCTION

Cats love aromatics - we all know about the catnip effect, right? But that's not the only herb cats enjoy, and there are many benefits to using herbs and aromatic extracts for cats. Properly used, they can help your beloved feline be happy and healthy in body, mind and soul. This book gives you easy-to-use, practical information on how herbs, hydrosols and essential oils can support your cat's wellbeing.

You may have heard that essential oils should never be used with cats? Well, this is not necessarily so, used correctly they can be a useful tool in your cat's wellness regime. In this book we will share how we use them with our own cats and those of clients, and how you too can use them safely for cats in your care.

Our recommended protocol is based on animal self-selection, a safe, effective and non-invasive system. Offering aromatic extracts like this provides environmental enrichment, as well as helping with a variety of conditions, whether physical, mental or emotional.

This simple, practical guide to aromatic botanicals for cats will give you confidence to use herbs, hydrosols and essential oils
- To support physical and mental wellbeing
- As natural remedies for daily care
- To increase immune function
- To enrich your cat's environment and reduce stress
- To give your cat a voice, by using self-selection

Nayana Morag and Julie-Anne Thorne

One of the things we love about aromatics and self-selection is that it gives your cat a voice and builds trustful communication. In reading your cats responses you connect on a deeper level and your cat can communicate with you what she wants and needs in order to thrive. Nayana is a qualified animal aromatherapist, working with animals and their people for over 20 years. Julie-Anne is an holistic feline practitioner, whose passion is being an interspecies interpreter, helping you hear and read what your cats are trying to share with you. In this book they combine skills so you and your cats can benefit from their experience. We all want to care for our cats the best we can. This book will empower you to do just that. Your cat will be shining with health and naturally contented from kitten-hood to the 'wise years'. Enjoy!

GOOD FOUNDATIONS

T he system you will learn in this book is based on allowing your cat to self-select the aromatics they need (zoopharmacognosy). We also believe that for true wellness it is important to look at health holistically and reduce stress through understanding your cats' biological needs. We are going to explore these concepts more thoroughly before diving into the aromatics. But before we go any further, let's answer that sticky question: are essential oils safe for cats?

Are essential oils safe for cats?

The quick answer is … it depends how you use them. Cats are more vulnerable to the misuse of essential oils than some animals, so we advise you do your research and learn how to use them safely with your cat. Also, we must remember that essential oils have been extracted from their natural environment and are much more potent than when found in nature. The key to safety is to differentiate between correct use and OVERUSE of essential oils.

Natural Cats

In a natural environment cats are exposed to essential oils daily because they are everywhere that plants grow. As cats walk through the undergrowth, rubbing against flowers, twigs, and leaves essential oils are released, albeit in minute amounts. When your cat rolls in a bed of catnip, she releases essential oils from the plant. Felis Catus is one of the most successful species on the planet, so must be an adaptable survivor, and unlikely to keel over at the first exposure to aromatic compounds. They wouldn't have got this far if they didn't have some tolerance. So why the fear?

Cats and Glucuronidation

It is well known in veterinary medicine that cats metabolise drugs and other toxins differently than other animals. This mechanism is not properly understood, despite being investigated since the 1950's. But we do know that the metabolic process of glucurodination, present in most mammals, is missing in cats.

Glucurodination is a detoxification process, whereby drugs and other substances are combined with glucuronic acid to form water-soluble compounds that are easier for the kidneys and bile to excrete.

Cats lack an enzyme called glucuronyl tranferase, which means they are less able to excrete certain chemical compounds, making them more sensitive to their use. In particular, cats take longer than dogs or humans to rid their bodies of some chemicals, such as phenols. Therefore, they are more likely to experience toxic overload if frequently exposed to these substances. Many essential oils contain phenolic compounds; therefore caution is required.

Overuse

It's true, there are reported cases of liver failure in cats after exposure to essential oils, but this has always been when undiluted essential oil has been applied topically, or a cat was forced to interact with the essential oil. A well-known case tells of someone who shaved her cats and applied undiluted tea tree oil to their skin to kill fleas. An obvious case of overuse.

There are also reports of cats who suffered liver congestion, digestive upset, lethargy and symptoms of neurological disease after being exposed to daily diffusion of essential oils in the home. Again, this is prolonged exposure to essential oils. The cats had no option to leave the room and get away from the molecules being released into the air. And remember, cats take longer to excrete toxins than other animals. Daily exposure to essential oils can overload a cat's liver.

To avoid a buildup of toxic metabolites in the body, or fatal toxic shock (at worst), you must be very cautious when using essential oil with cats. Especially avoid the more pungent, camphoraceous oils, such as eucalyptus, pine, or tea tree, (although tea tree is safe to use as a hydrosol) or anything high in phenols. Always make sure a cat can leave the room to a source of fresh air if you are diffusing essential oils, and NEVER apply topically, unless under professional supervision.

Safe Use

Every medicine can be toxic if misused. The safe way to use essential oils with cats is to dilute highly and allow your cats to choose how, when, and with what to interact. Trust their innate sense of what is good. When you do this, you will find that inhalation is the preferred method of interaction, and a tiny amount is enough to trigger healing. Hundreds of cats feeling happier and healthier are testimony to this system.

Having said that, if you prefer to leave essential oils to the professionals, hydrosols and herbs are safer for the layman to use with their cats. We encourage you to explore all the aromatic extracts. Using self-selection, you can't go wrong.

Listen to the one who knows best!

If we use nature's guidance and allow cats the choice to interact with aromatics when and how they like, they will cause no harm and have many benefits. This is especially important for indoor only cats. More about self-selection in the next chapter.

Why the Fear?

The fear of using essential oils with cats arose from incidents of over-exposure.

For example:

- Topical application of tea tree essential oil to a shaved cat for flea control. The cat died.
- One drop of undiluted peppermint oil applied to the tummy of a cat that had hairballs. The cat became very ill.
- Pine oil added to a litter tray. The cat developed signs of toxicity within a week.

Zoopharmacognosy

(Zoo = animal, pharma = medicine, cognosy = knowledge)
Zoopharmacognosy is a very long word for animal self-medication. This scientific discipline studies an animal's instinctive drive to seek out the healing herbs and minerals he or she needs.

Animals are said to be self-medicating when they eat something that is not a normal part of their diet. This can be a plant, fungi, soil or clay.

The most common domestic example is a cat eating grass to cleanse their digestive tract. Observe carefully when your cat eats grass, and you will see that she is selecting her grasses very carefully.

More exotic examples are: monkeys eating bitter herbs to cleanse parasites; macaques rubbing aromatic plants into their fur to prevent fleas and heal skin sores; birds using insect repellent plants to line their nests; and elephants using clay as plasters for wounds. There are many more examples being observed as scientists study the phenomenon.

Scientists assume that animal self-medication is based on the hedonic response and is driven by "that which feels good". Differences in body chemistry cause animals to find substances tasty if their bodies need a healing compound. When the body is healed, the plant no longer tastes good.

For more on this head to the recommended resource section at the back of the book.

Self-selection

Domestic cats retain the innate ability to select plant medicines. Such a useful biological survival mechanism is not easily lost. When working with aromatics, we respect this instinctive ability and let cats select between aromatics we offer them.

The aromatics your cat chooses can help you understand the root of what might be bothering her, or if she needs more support with something. For instance, if you think your cat 'isn't quite right', you could offer a few dried herbs. If she selects valerian root, which helps with pain and stress/anxiety, you could then offer comfrey leaf, a pain remedy and chamomile for stress. If she selects the comfrey it points towards pain, if she selects the chamomile, she is pointing you towards anxiety related aromatics. When you give your cat the opportunity to tell you what she needs you can offer aromatics that support her emotional and physical needs.

During our combined 35 years of experience, self-selection has proved itself to be a safe, effective and powerful healing method that has many advantages. Not the least of which is that cats love it!

The holistic view

Healing works best when you look at the whole picture and consider all factors in the cat's life and history. This holistic view is fundamental to the way we work.

You may have had the frustrating experience of multiple vet visits for the same problem (we have!) Each visit the prescription is changed. For a while there might even be some improvement in the condition, but soon you are back to square one: itchy skin, fungal ears, or whatever problem brought you to the vet in the first place. Or maybe you got rid of the itching, but you are soon back at the vets trying to get on top of Irritable Bowel Syndrome (IBS).

This familiar scenario is a result of the way modern medicine focusses on disease symptoms, without addressing their causes. Allopathic medicine absolutely has its place in animal care, but for the best results we need to find the root of the problem, which may not be immediately obvious.

The holistic view sees body, mind, emotions, and environment, as one interactive system. With this view in mind we can see that both of the problems mentioned above arise from the same underlying imbalance, which is probably the diet. If you adjust your cat's diet you are likely to see both problems resolve. Using an holistic approach, symptoms become clues to detect where the system has broken down and needs support. Our aim is to help your cats rebalance their whole system, so they can heal themselves.

Stress & Wellness

We strongly believe that for your cat to be truly healthy, you must reduce stresses wherever possible. This is usually easy to do with small changes in management and diet. Stress is the prime cause of dis-ease for animals, and every domestic animal is subject to small stresses on a daily basis, simply because they are not free to choose.

Not all stress is bad, it's a natural part of any animal's life. Even hunting, or chasing toys provokes stress on a physiological level. As the chase/hunt switches are turned on adrenalin levels are raised and joints and muscles are stressed by running, turning and stopping. But this sort of stress is natural, short term and not problematic. Too many stresses, or chronic stress such as our domestic cats are often exposed to, leads to distress, opening the door for disease.

Aromatics can help cats cope with the everyday stresses of normal life, such as family changes, moving home, or exposure to viruses. However, for best results, be aware of what stresses cats, and your cat in particular, and keep it to a minimum.

One of the major causes of stress for any animal is lack of self-determination. We love our cats, but our concern for their well-being often means we restrict their freedom and limit their choices.

You may not be able to let your cat out of your home, but you can let her participate in her own health care. Letting your cat self-select aromatic extracts reduces stress and improves health. Stress reduction plus aromatics is a powerful healing combination.

Major causes of stress for modern cats:

- Inappropriate diet (cats should eat a meat-based diet, either wet or raw food)
- Over vaccination
- Chemical flea treatments
- Miscommunication with a guardian
- Mis-understood expectations about their behaviour
- Lack of stimulation
- Over stimulation
- Multi-cat households
- Lack of territory

Nayana Morag and Julie-Anne Thorne

THE AROMATICS

In this section we will explore the different types of aromatics and when to use each one.

Quality and Sustainability

But first, let's talk about sustainability. It is always important when buying any of the botanicals to consider how they were grown and produced. Wherever possible buy organically grown, especially the herbs. If something is marked as wild-crafted make sure it was harvested consciously, without causing environmental damage. Many herbs are becoming endangered due to indiscriminate over-harvesting to satisfy the herbal remedy market. None of the plants we list in this book are on the endangered or scarce list. Any reputable supplier will be able to give you that information when asked.

HERBS

What is a herb?

For many of you 'herb' means a green leafy plant, or perhaps something you use for flavouring food. For our purposes here, a herb is any plant, or part of it, that is therapeutic.

Herbs are chemically complex with an abundance of active constituents and a wide range of therapeutic actions. Because of this, herbs can be used to address a variety of health issues and support many levels of the body, including the nervous system.

Herbs cross the line between food and medicine because in many cases they are nutritive as well as therapeutic. They work more slowly than the other aromatics because they are mostly absorbed through the digestive system. The exception being those which are also aromatic. Cats appear to be more sensitive to the aromatic level of the herbs, as they don't always choose to eat herbs, often just sitting near them. Either way, they work.

Use herbs for Daily Wellbeing

In a natural environment cats have daily exposure to herbs and plants. They walk through them, or roll on them, or perhaps chew them a little. This is completely natural behaviour for a cat, part of how she takes care of herself, and one that she may not have the opportunity to enjoy in a domestic environment. You can satisfy this natural urge with a "herb garden" which provides immediate stress relief and is easy for you to create, as described below.

Herbs, a gentle way to support healing.

I worked with a cat who was vomiting after food and at various points during the day. The vet couldn't find any issue and advised a change of food. The guardian asked me to help. We offered a herb garden with catnip, peppermint, nettle and chickweed. Sammy selected chickweed, which supports the digestive tract. He spent quite some time lying with his throat over the chickweed herb. He didn't vomit for the next two days.
Julie-Anne

Dried or fresh herbs are a safe and natural way to introduce your cat to self-selection. Even if your cat is perfectly healthy, she will enjoy having access to plants in this way. Offering herbs also provides environmental enrichment for your cat, especially indoor cats. And seeing what they select is an easy way for you to assess their current emotional and physical state.

You can put down herbs for your cat if she looks a bit "off" or any time there is a stressful situation. For instance, if they were chased by a neighbourhood cat, or you had a visitor in your home. Putting down a herb garden allows the cat to relax and release their stress.

You can also offer a herb garden if you are concerned your cat is suffering, either physically, mentally or emotionally. For example, ongoing support with arthritis.

How to use Herbs

The easiest way to give your cat access to herbs, no matter where you live, is to make a herb mat with dried herbs. To do this, lay a blanket or towel on the floor with dried herbs/flowers in each corner. We call this a "herb garden". Your cat is free to interact with the herbs as she chooses and may rub, roll or sniff on each aromatic, or just choose to lie there enjoying the fragrance. There is no right or wrong, your cat is taking what she needs in the way she needs it. You can also use fresh herbs in the same way: parsley, basil, lemongrass and marjoram are popular choices.

Dried herb gardens can be left down as part of the cat's day to day environment, just like a scratching post. Check the herbs regularly in case they need to be topped up or removed. When you are laying the herb garden down make sure it is in a quiet area, away from household activity. It's important the cat has the opportunity to take herself away from the family to a place where she feels safe, because she can feel vulnerable as she starts to process and heal.

When offering a herb garden in multi-cat households keep other cats away. Preferably put down multiple gardens so all the cats can enjoy their own herb time and won't have an excuse to fight over resources.

Herbs are the first choice for daily maintenance for any cat, and extremely safe to use.

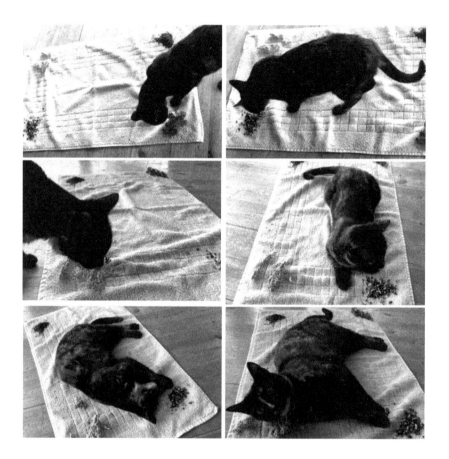

Kestra enjoys her herb garden of catnip, dandelion root, and yarrow. She ignores the peppermint

Storage and Safety

Herbs should be stored in a cool dark cupboard, preferably in well-sealed glass jars. Make sure moisture can't get in. Herbs that are crushed or powdered don't last as long as whole or cut herbs. General guidelines are 1-3 years, with leaves deteriorating more quickly than roots.

It's always preferable to buy in smaller quantities more frequently so the herbs retain as many active principles as possible.

When buying herbs make sure they are human grade. Herbs can sometimes be treated with perfumes to make their scent more intense, like those used for potpourri, these are not suitable for our purposes. Buy organic where you can.

HYDROSOLS

What is a hydrosol?

Hydrosol (also called hydrolat) is generally the water part of the steam distillation of essential oils. After the bulk of the essential oil is removed, the water (hydrosol) that is left behind contains the gentler, water-soluble plant molecules, and minute traces of essential oil.

There are also smaller artisan distillers who distill plants solely for the water (hydrosol) and the essential oil is not necessarily removed. This is sometimes known as aromatic water. Aromatic water contains higher levels of essential oil, so needs to be diluted more than hydrosol that is an essential oil by-product. However, hydrosol distilled as a primary product contains a wider range of active molecules and is generally better quality.

When to use hydrosols

Hydrosols can be used in the same way as herbs, to reduce stress and enhance environment. The advantage of hydrosols is that they are more easily absorbed by the body, so work more quickly than herbs. Hydrosols are a safe way to offer cats volatile aromatics as they contain the gentle, water soluble molecules of the plant, which are more easily excreted than essential oils.

If you feel your cat needs further support after offering herbs, or you want to remedy something more serious, try a hydrosol.

Hydrosols are gentle on the skin and easily digested, so once diluted they are a safe option for topical or internal use. The traces of volatile essential oil are mostly absorbed through the olfactory system, so you have multiple pathways of absorption, increasing their ability to provoke healing.

Once diluted, you can use them topically to treat skin irritation or pests. They can also be used as a cat-safe air freshener for your home.

How to use hydrosols

Unlike essential oils, hydrosols dissolve in water. You can put a few drops in a bowl of water and let your cat sniff or drink it whenever she likes. You can leave a calming hydrosol for her if she gets anxious when you go out. Or a little ginger hydrosol to ease the discomfort of arthritis. You can relieve tension in multi-cat households by leaving bowls with diluted hydrosol where each cat can interact with it, as and when they need.

Hydrosol is often sold in a spray bottle, so you can just spritz a little into a bowl rather than using drops. You can also spray on your hands and see if your cat wants to rub against them, or through the auric field.

You can also use hydrosols to help cats who don't want to interact with humans, as you can add the hydrosol to a bowl of water, then leave the area. If you add a hydrosol to a bowl of water always make sure you have a plain bowl of water available as well, so they have a choice.

Cat enjoying a bowl of diluted hydrosol, just lying close, looking at the bowl and inhaling the aromatic molecules

Safety and Storage

Be aware that sometimes hydrosols are called floral water. However, often a product sold as floral water, is just plain water with essential oil added. This is not the same as a true hydrosol and is potentially dangerous for your cat.

Purchase only from those who can guarantee botanical purity and quality control. Some companies also add preservatives to the hydrosol, be sure to check that you are buying preservative free. Hydrosols are best stored in glass bottles, in a cool dark place. Ideally not a fridge but a cellar. Hydrosols produced from highly aromatic plants, such as rosemary, last longer than hydrosols from soft flowers, such as cornflower or neroli.

It is generally recommended not to use hydrosols for therapeutic purposes if they are more than a year old. If you can see floating strings of 'stuff' in your hydrosol it is "off". However, you can still use them as household cleaners if you pass them through a coffee filter to clean them up.

Check with your supplier for recommended shelf life on each item.

Use hydrosols for ongoing problems, or routine healthcare. Great for reducing group pressures, for cats who don't want to interact with humans and for skin problems.

What is an essential oil?

In nature, essential oils can be found in either the seeds, roots, leaves, resin, bark or flowers of aromatic plants. They are secondary metabolites (not essential for the plants survival) and in different plants they have different functions. For example, to protect from microbes or attract insects for pollination, or to repel herbivores.

Essential oils are the fragrant molecules that are released when you break a lavender plant, or open an orange, designed to be inhaled. Essential oils are highly volatile, light weight and penetrative. When inhaled (the way cats normally choose to use them) the molecules enter directly into the regions of the brain concerned with emotions and memory, and the endocrine system. The nervous system transforms the messages from these aromatic chemicals into physical responses in the body, such as the anti-inflammatory, relaxation, or anti-allergenic responses.

Essential oils are most commonly extracted from the plant by steam distillation. Plant material is put in a large vat, steam is then forced through it under pressure, condensed and collected as water. The essential oil collects on top of the water and is separated out. The remaining water is the hydrosol

Essential oils are also produced using solvent extraction, in which case they are known as absolutes. The vast majority of essential oils are produced for the fragrance and flavouring industries, which demand high yield and low cost. Essential oils suitable for therapeutic use are distilled with care, slowly and at a lower temperature, so more of the healing molecules remain intact.

Unfortunately, many essential oils are adulterated, usually by adding synthetic fragrances or a cheaper essential oil with a similar fragrance. This is especially true of the more expensive oils, such as rose, or those in high demand, like french lavender.

The best way to guarantee you are using good quality oils is to purchase from a reputable supplier who is also a trained aromatherapist, can tell you where the plant was grown and how it was distilled, and guarantee botanical purity. In the Appendix you'll find a list of recommended suppliers.

Why risk more?

One of the first times I used essential oils with a cat was when I was training. Our cat had been off his food for about 36 hours, a very unusual thing for this fat cat. I held an open bottle with 1 drop of carrot seed (Daucus carota) in 10 ml of sunflower oil. The cat walked past the bottle, took a little sniff, turned around and walked back to tuck in to his food dish. This experience, and many similar ones through the years, are why I am so adamant about the dilution of essential oils. If a tiny amount works, why would you use more? *Nayana*

When we consider the place of an essential oil in nature, we can understand why such apparently small doses can be effective. It takes kilos of plant matter to produce even a small amount of essential oil, even for high yielding plants. For those with less essential oil, like rose, it can take tons. Before humans interfere, essential oils are just a tiny fraction of the plant, buffered (diluted) by a large amount of plant matter. Which is why it's important to dilute well before use, just as nature intended.

When to use Essential oils

Essential oils are powerful medicines and their place in your natural pharmacy should reflect that. Use a small amount infrequently. They are best when you need a remedy that will work quickly, such as for an immediate immune boost, or for shock.

However, there are some useful essential oils that can't be found as hydrosol, or perhaps you don't have the hydrosol and do have the essential oil, in which case well-diluted essential, oil offered for inhalation, is a good option.

How to use essential oils

Essential oils should be diluted at least 1 drop to 10 ml (2 teaspoons) before offering to your cat. They are also effective at 1 drop in 30 ml (2 tablespoons). You can also put one drop on a small cloth, and leave it hanging where the cat can smell it when she wants, but make sure she can leave the area to a source of fresh air if she chooses.

Essential Oils are potent medicines and can be used with cats in high dilution via inhalation, for healing and emotional support.

Kestra inhales essential oil, diluted 1 drop in 30 ml of carrier oil

Vegetable and Herbal Oils

What is a vegetable oil?

Vegetable oils are extracted from the nuts, seeds or kernels of plants. Some of them, such as hemp or neem, are therapeutic in their own right. Others have little or no inherent fragrance or therapeutic action and make a perfect, neutral carrier oil for essential oils, especially for emotional/behavioural problems. They are also nutritious in many cases.

If you have only one vegetable oil in your kit, opt for cold-pressed sunflower or jojoba. Good quality vegetable oils should not be heated at any point in the production process, so always use traditional cold-pressed oil. Since pesticides and other chemical residues are easily carried over in the extraction process, choose organic whenever possible. Do not use the highly processed vegetable oils you find in supermarkets.

What is an herbal oil?

Herbal oil, also known as macerated or infused oil, is made by soaking medicinal herbs in a cold-pressed vegetable oil, such as sunflower or olive oil. Lipid (fat) soluble molecules are drawn out of the plant into the oil. These herbal oils are true aromatic extracts with powerful healing qualities.

You can use them for diluting essential oils but they can also be used on their own in the long-term care of conditions such as arthritis, or for wound care, and some of them are safe to use topically with cats.

Vegetable and herbal macerated oils are nutritive and healing. They work on their own or as carrier oils.

Storage and shelf life

The lifespan of hydrosols and essential oils can vary tremendously from one botanical to the next, from one distillation to the next, and from one supplier to the next. Key factors that can directly affect the shelf life include:

- The composition of natural chemical constituents present in the essential oil or hydrosol
- The method of distillation
- The conditions and care used during the distillation
- The quality and harvesting of the plant material
- The care in bottling, storage and handling of the aromatics throughout the supply chain
- The storage conditions once you have received it.

Each item has its own shelf life. Some of the more delicate carrier oils start to oxidize after 3 months (flaxseed). Some essential oils improve with age. As a general guide, the heavier, thicker essential oils, like vetiver, last longer. The lightweight citrus and pine essential oils last for a year

Storing Aromatics

- Aromatics need to be stored in a cool dark, animal proof place.
- Keep aromatics away from direct sunlight and heat.
- All aromatics are best stored in glass bottles. Essential oils will destroy plastic containers.
- Hydrosols must be refrigerated in hot climates, although root cellar temperature is ideal.
- Dried herbs need to be kept away from children in either plastic or glass containers out of direct sunlight.
- The more air there is in the bottle the quicker essential oils and hydrosols degrade. It's best to buy in smaller bottles.
- Avoid introducing bacteria into the bottles. Don't put your fingers on the top of an open bottle of hydrosol or carrier oil.
- Decant hydrosols and carrier/herbal oils into smaller bottles before offering to animals to keep the storage bottles clean and bacteria free.

Because many of the factors that impact shelf life begin with the botanical planting/harvesting, distillation and initial handling/storage, it's important to shop with essential oil suppliers that you trust. Some essential oil suppliers are able to share the date of distillation for each lot of essential oil they maintain. Responsible sellers store aromatics in conditions far superior to those we as consumers are capable of, another good reason to buy small quantities at a time.

How to Use Aromatics, Step by Step

The best way to keep your cat healthy and happy is to offer aromatics on a regular basis. If you have a garden, you can plant aromatic plants and simple herbs and grasses for your cat to enjoy. Even if you only have a patio or balcony you can plant up a pot for them. But if growing plants is not your thing, it is the non-growing season, or you have an indoor only cat, you can lay down a herb garden, as we have said. Or put out a selection of hydrosols. Or both.

Offering aromatics regularly is the key to ensuring you support the ever-changing needs of your cat. The more often you offer aromatics, the less chance there is of a problem developing.

Nevertheless, however well we care for our animals, sometimes things happen. Maybe you moved to a new house, or your family constellation changed, or your cat is ageing, or got into a fight. Any of these things can cause your cat's behaviour or health to be challenged.

To address a specific issue, make a short list of the aromatics that are most likely to help, using the charts and profiles in this book. Then present them to your cat so she can make her choice.

Here's how to do it, step by step.

1. Make your shortlist

Think carefully about what you aim to achieve and set a healing intention. Don't just look at aromatics for the present symptoms. Remember, symptoms are just a clue to the underlying imbalance. To clear the root cause, look for the aromatics that match the whole picture: past and present, physical and emotional.

The more you clarify your aims, the easier it will be to select the aromatics. If you say, "I want to make my cat feel better", you will have endless possibilities. When you look at the whole picture and include all physical, emotional and behavioural factors you narrow your choices.

"I want to help my cat's stiffness, she also seems to be more fearful since we moved house, and she has dandruff", sets a clear goal and will help you find the aromatics you need.

2. Select your aromatics

Once you have set your goal, look at the list of Aromatics for Specific Conditions on page 155, and check which aromatics are suggested for:

- Stiffness and/or pain
- Fear
- Confidence
- Dandruff.

Sometimes you will find one essential oil or hydrosol that covers all your goals. Other times it will take two or three different aromatics to cover everything.

Next, look at the Aromatic Cross Reference Chart and see which of the possible aromatics most closely matches your cat's issues. The more conditions in each box that match your cat, the more likely it is to be the best one for the job.

Aim to have a short list of 3-5 different aromatics. Your cat will probably select one or two. You can offer a mixture of essential oils, hydrosols and herbs.

Here is the shortlist for our example:

- Cedarwood (*Cedrus deodora*) for stiffness, circulation stimulant, fear, grounding after change of home, dandruff
- Angelica root (*Angelica archangelica*) circulation stimulant for stiffness, to feel protected (fear)
- Geranium (*Pelargonium graveolens*) for scurfy skin, lack of confidence, moving home
- Valerian (*Valeriana officinalis*) fear, anti-inflammatory, fearful aggression
- Hemp seed carrier oil

3. Give your cat a choice

Let your cat smell each of the aromatics on your shortlist, one by one. With the **lid on**, hold the bottle a short distance away from the cat and gauge her response. She will move towards the ones she likes with her nose, maybe lick her lip a little or gently close her eyes. If she doesn't want the oil she will walk away. Or you can place all the bottles/herbs in a circle on the floor. Let your cat walk through the bottles and see which ones she selects. This takes close observation, as just pausing by a bottle can be an indication of selection.

Dilute any essential oil or hydrosol selected as described below and offer them again one by one. This time let her interact with the oil/hydrosol however she chooses. Leave the aromatic beside her until she is either fast asleep and does not respond when you move the extract, or she walks away.

If you are using herbs or hydrosols you can leave them down where the cat can interact with them when and how she chooses. Refresh the hydrosol every day and make sure clean water is also available.

In this sequence Amokay obviously selects the calendula macerate.
She lies down to process it, after having a good sniff. Note her eyes are
still open

How to dilute essential oils

Essential oils should be diluted 1 drop in 10 to 30 ml (2 teaspoons
- 2 tablespoons) in a carrier oil. Pour the carrier oil into an amber
glass bottle of appropriate size. The bottle should have a screw on
cap, to keep the diluted oil fresh.

Label the bottle with the names of the essential oil and carrier oil and the dilution level. Wrap a piece of clear sticky tape around the label so that, when oily, it doesn't slip off. If stored in a cool dark place, the diluted oil will stay fresh for about 3 months.

Dilute each essential oil separately. Do not blend. Your cat needs the freedom to interact individually with each extract. If you mix the oils, your cat is likely to refuse the blend when she goes off only one of the oils. Or, if she is really desperate, she may continue to take the blend just for the one oil she needs, increasing the risk of sensitization or irritation.

How to dilute hydrosol

Fill a small bowl or saucer with water (about 100ml/1/3rd cup) add 3 or 4 drops of the selected hydrosol. Don't stir, so the cat can choose the stronger smelling area near the slowly dispersing drops or lick/smell further away, where it is less strong. If your cat looks back at the undiluted bottle after smelling the bowl, add a few more drops of hydrosol, up to 10 drops per 100 ml.

Create Success

When working with a cat on a particular problem, set yourself up for success. Make this quality one on one time with your cat, a quiet healing time for you to share together.

Offer in an area way from any potential distractions or perceived threats. Cats need time and space to heal, and they can sometimes feel vulnerable as they process the remedies.

Choose a time when there are no other interactions or excitements, such as meal times, or someone coming home from work. Exclude other animals if possible. You can always let other household animals in after the session has finished and your cat removes herself (you may find they enjoy the remedies too!)

Take time out of your busy schedule to enjoy this process with your cat. Their timetable is different to humans, a cat can spend up to 40 minutes working with one remedy. Give yourself time to watch and observe, and enjoy your cat selecting the aromatics. Patience is the key to success.

A little lick of   *This expression is a*
the lips is a "yes"   *strong "yes", mouth*
slighty open as she really
takes in the smell.

Understanding your cat's responses

The foundation of self-selection is interpreting your cat's responses. We are going to talk you through the various possibilities so you can see how easy it is.

A cat's response may be so subtle you think nothing is happening. Or she may want to come over and rub her body on the oil bottle. This depends on your cat's character and the nature of her imbalance. As long as she chooses to stay in the room with the aromatics it is considered a positive response.

Trust that she knows how to regulate her intake by proximity to the aromatic.

Let her move around and set her own distance from the aromatics. Don't chase her around with the oil/hydrosol, as this can cause a negative response. Just sit quietly and wait to see what unfolds.

Inhalation

We consider inhalation the most powerful way to deliver aromatics, since they go straight into the brain via the olfactory system. The brain then sends messages via neuro-transmitters, which trigger the appropriate responses in the body. That is why just smelling an essential oil can be enough to reduce pain, balance hormones, relieve itching, etc.

In an inhalation response your cat will lie down quietly and go into a trance-like state, head lowered, eyes slightly closed as her brain chemistry is affected by the remedy. It may look like she is just lying there doing nothing. But if you observe carefully, you will notice her breathing has slightly changed, her ears have softened, nostrils may flare and eyes slowly flickering, half closed, or slowly blinking.

*Kestra in trance. There is one drop of
diluted essential oil on the hand*

If you are unsure whether your cat is engaging with the remedy, slowly move the bottle away from her. If you notice her nose follow the bottle or she glances at you quickly, bring the bottle back and keep it still for her.

If there is no reaction when you move the bottle, replace the lid and wait for your cat to return from her relaxed space before offering another oil/hydrosol. Do not hurry the process and do not try to offer other oils until she has "come back", this may take half an hour or so. You can leave her to it.

Sometimes cats may release a big sigh, or start to purr when you simply bring an oil out of your collection. If this happens, put the closed bottle near by and let her sit with it.

Another way you can leave an essential oil safely with your cat is to put a small drop on a paper aroma stick (like the ones you get in perfume shops), or a small piece of fabric, such as a cut up t-shirt or face cloth. This allows the cat to return to the fragrance as and when she needs to.

Topical

Your cat may occasionally indicate a particular spot on her body by putting her nose to it, scratching or moving into you with her body. Often, she is indicating an acupressure point, or a spot that is painful. In this case you can offer to see if your cat would like you to touch the spot with a finger tip covered with the diluted essential oil or hydrosol.

Julie-Anne had an experience where a cat selected Jasmine essential oil and indicated he wanted it applied topically. She mixed one drop of essential oil with 10 ml/1 tablespoon of sunflower oil and rubbed it all over both hands. She then sat with her hands open and the cat rubbed his flank into her fingertips. The cat was drooling and purring loudly, the feline guardian said she had never seen the cat so happy. The cat proceeded to sleep for 6 hours! This is a rare interaction, but does happen.

Hydrosols can be used in the same way. Spray or rub the hydrosol on your hands, hold your hands open and see if the cat wants to rub into them. Or perhaps she just wants you to pass your hands through the auric field, a few centimetres from the body. Cats are very sensitive to the energy of remedies.

Oral

Oral interaction is more likely when there is a physical or digestive problem. Hydrosols, herbal and vegetable oils, herbs and nutritive powders can all be taken orally. Hydrosols diluted in water 3-10 drops to 100 ml of water can be left in a quiet spot for cats to interact with as they like. Cats often prefer to interact with the aromatics when they are not being observed, so will come back to the dish for a drink or sniff when no-one is looking, or quite commonly they will curl up to sleep beside the dish.

Drinking diluted hydrosol, 3 drops in 50ml water

Vegetable and herbal oils can be offered on a saucer, up to 10 ml per day.

Powdered herbs can be offered for selection, (it's good to offer 2 or 3 at once). If your cat smells any of them intensely, add 1 teaspoon to a saucer and dribble water over it, or sunflower oil. Don't mix well, so there are areas that are thicker and some where the water has run off the herb. This way the cat can regulate dosage.

Saying "NO"

Cats can be subtle in their signs when working with aromatics, except when they don't want a remedy. In this instance they will make it perfectly clear, as only a cat can. Most commonly they say 'no thank you' by leaving the room. Don't immediately pack up your kit, because she may return after thinking about it to see what else you have on offer. But put away the oil she rejected and wait for her to return to you.

If you offer a remedy and the cat moves away slightly but stays in the room, and looks in your direction they just need to process the remedy from a distance.

If they stay in the room, give you a haughty stare and bury their nose under a paw, or cushion, especially if their back is towards you, it is also a no. Try again later, or perhaps just put down a herb garden, which will work on a gentler level.

Let the cat be your guide. The more you play around with it, the easier it becomes to recognise the responses and as your cat understands you are listening, she will tell you more clearly what she needs.

It's really a joy.

Extreme reactions

On rare occasions you may see a cat exhibit a response that gives you cause for concern. Reactions such as growling, yowling, howling, a hissing outburst or attempts at biting. These are not signs that your cat does not like the remedy, it is in fact the opposite. They are signs of deep healing and emotional release. In our experience it helps to dilute the remedy you are working with, but also to offer additional emotionally supportive remedies such as angelica root, jasmine and rose.

Allow your cat the time and space to process this energy and emotion. Keep your energy calm and relaxed, be careful not to stroke your cat whilst they are in this state, talk to them in a soothing voice, giving lots of verbal reassurance. After the initial outburst cats tend to settle, usually with a deep sigh, going to sleep or they may leave the room to take time for themselves. Know that you have helped your cat with deep-seated emotional blockages and energy shifting. This type of reaction is more common with chronic issues or previous trauma.

Changing Interests
Once you have had an initial session and your cat has selected some remedies, offer them every day until she shows no more interest. You will find that your cat interacts differently with each aromatic from session to session. This is what we want.

Extreme reactions help to shift energy.

I worked with a cat who was shot by an air rifle a couple of years ago. She started by ingesting dried valerian root and comfrey leaf to ease her pain and discomfort. We then wanted to work on re-building her trust in humans now that she was in her forever home. We offered dried linden blossom which helps to build trust. At first, she seemed agitated, which was out of character. Then she moved to sit near it, hissed twice, sighed and settled down. It was a wonderful display of selection, processing and healing. Herbs can be so powerful. *Julie-Anne*

In the beginning she may be intensely interested in one botanical and less interested in others. But this interest can vary from day to day, depending on her needs. As treatment progresses your cat should lose interest in all the aromatics, normally within three days to a week of the first session. In some cases, your cat will lose interest after one session, especially if the problem was not deep seated. By the time your cat loses interest completely you will normally see a significant reduction of the problem.

Signs of remedy selection	Signs of selection that suggest need for further dilution	Signs of no selection
Licking the air	Hissing outburst	No change in reaction or behaviour
Swallowing	Biting	Leaving the room
Yawning	Growling	Burying their head
Closing eyes/blinking	Crying	
Moving towards the remedy	Howling	
Rolling and stretching	Shallow panting	
Lowering of the head/softening of the body	Backing away from a remedy	
Laying down/stretching out		
Stillness/trance like state		
Nostrils flaring		
Slow/deep breathing/ large exhale		

Safe usage

Aromatics are a safe option for your cat IF you allow them to self-select and you understand the safety parameters of the different type of aromatics. However, here are a few more specific safety points to note.

The most common problem

Anything can cause harm when over or mis-used. For cats this is usually over-use of topical applications. But as we've mentioned above, having a cat in an enclosed area while diffusing can also cause sensitization, or a toxic build up in the liver.

That's why we advocate against regular use of essential oil, reed, plug-in or wax melt diffusers in the home.

Changing nature

Although self-selection is based on natural processes, an essential oil or dried herb is not the same as the live plant in nature. We have removed much of its bulk and many of nature's own regulatory measures. Thus, it's important to dilute essential oils and hydrosols and regulate your cats intake of herbs accordingly.

Furthermore, self-selection is based on taking something until you feel better. Sometimes the trigger for the "not good" feeling is something in the environment. For example, diet or household. If you do not remove the source of the problem, your cat may not know when to stop. This increases the risk of sensitization or toxic overload.

Know when to call in the professionals

If your cat has disease symptoms, it is crucial to consult with a veterinarian as soon as possible. While natural medicine is great for your home pharmacy, sometimes you need stronger, allopathic medicine. Building a good relationship with your vet ensures that your cat has the best possible care. Together you can work out a treatment plan

Nayana Morag and Julie-Anne Thorne

that includes aromatics and gives your cat an holistic approach to its care.

Some basic guidelines for safety's sake

- Allow your cat to self-select
- Never blend aromatics together, keep each item separate so you cat can select how to interact with each one
- Never apply an essential oil topically to your cat
- Use high grade essential oils, hydrosols and herbs from a reputable supplier
- In the unlikely event of your cat showing a negative reaction, such as skin irritation or shortness of breath, immediately discontinue use and contact a vet
- Store aromatics in a cool, dark place with their caps firmly closed
- Do not use on pregnant cats
- Pay attention to the cautions and safety issues with each aromatic
- Finally, whatever you do, when you have a problem, don't go to the internet and canvas the opinions of well-meaning but unqualified people. They have no formal training in animal aromatherapy and do not specifically know your cat. Always seek the advice of a trained animal professional.

Losing control

One last thing before we move on. We have found that the hardest thing about allowing cats to self-select aromatics is letting go of the notion that YOU know best! We may think something is wrong and want to fix it, it's part of our basic instinct to care and nurture. But in basically healthy cats, most things get better with time and patience. And sometimes things that concern us, or we think are problems, are actually nature's way of healing.

Cats are in tune with their instincts, they know exactly what they need. We need to respect that and hear their voice. Always let them choose to interact with the aromatics, or not. Giving the cat a choice in his/her treatment is the best thing you can do for your cat's wellbeing and will change the quality of your relationship.

Chewing on wild grasses in a herb bouquet

What Can I Use Aromatics For?

Environmental Control

Do you enjoy diffusing essential oils in your house? You may have heard this can be dangerous for cats? If you diffuse or have any type of air freshener (plug in, wax melts, scented candles or reed based), always ensure the cat can remove herself to a place of fresh, circulating air. This is especially important for indoor only cats, and we encourage you to limit diffusion to an absolute minimum.

As we mentioned at the start, cats take longer to process toxins through their body. If the cat is unable to remove herself from the chemicals (natural or synthetic) the toxic effect can build up over time which could prove to be fatal.

Limit infectious disease

Having said that, diffusing essential oils for targeted medicinal reasons can be useful. For instance, if you want to limit the spread of viruses, such as in a cattery or rescue shelter you can diffuse anti-viral essential oils for 10 minutes or so. Cats should be removed from the area while the diffuser runs and only returned after the air has cleared.

Creating calm

In multi-cat households you can create a calm environment by putting down bowls with diluted hydrosol. Peppermint and roman chamomile are favourites for this job. Also, having access to herb gardens can help to minimize the stress or anxiety of a multi-cat household, Valerian, chamomile and calendula are all good herbs to support stress and anxiety. But ultimately, what you use will always depend on the particular characters of the cats involved.

Bug Control

Natural resistance

Healthy cats, fed fresh or raw food, are more able to resist bugs. By contrast, poor diet, high stress levels, flea treatments and vaccines lower immunity and make infestation and irritation more likely. Regularly offering aromatics keeps the immune system in tip-top shape, ready to repel bugs and the diseases they often carry.

Make your own natural repellent

But in some climates and some seasons bugs can get the best of even the healthiest cats. In this situation, aromatics are your best ally in the fight against fleas, ticks and mosquitoes, because you can make your own 100% natural repellents.

Our favourite method is to mix:
- ½ cup diatomaceous earth (food grade)
- ¼ cup neem leaf powder
- ¼ cup kaolin clay.

Rub a little into the scruff and around the tail, so any fleas pass through it. A little goes a long way and weekly application should be enough. Make sure you and your cat don't breathe in the diatomaceous earth as you apply.

If you are unable to get hold of the components mentioned above, you can use gel, although cats often don't enjoy this so much. Mix one to two drops of neem oil into 50 ml of very thin hydrosol gel. Neem oil is one of nature's strongest insecticides. Since the smell can be unpleasant, or even offensive to some people, you definitely need to dilute well. But it really works.

You can use sweet smelling insect repellent hydrosols to help mask the neem smell. Geranium and lemongrass are renowned insect repellents. But, again, each cat has her own preference and many aromatics repel bugs, so offer a selection of hydrosols and let her choose. See more about making hydrosol gel below.

Rub a small amount through the coat only if you know your cat has fleas. Concentrate on the areas where the bugs travel: the scruff, between the legs and around the ears.

Always get your cat's permission before application. Never force a remedy on your cat. Give them a choice in their treatment.

Behavioural concerns

As we've mentioned, remedies will only bring lasting relief if the stressor, or cause of the issue, has been identified and resolved. Here are some common behaviour related problems we encounter, and simple steps you can take to reduce the stress that creates them. If you are experiencing any of the following conditions with your cat, offer aromatics as listed, but also consider seeking additional professional support to help you both.

Anxiety

Anxiety can be subtle in cats. From sleeping with one eye open to monitor their surroundings, to hiding away or over-vocalising. If your cat is suffering with anxiety, be patient and gentle.

Help the cat to build confidence in her surroundings. Provide high vantage points and places to hide. Allow the cat to come to you for physical attention if she chooses and use a calm, soothing voice when communicating with the cat. Top aromatics for anxiety: Calendula, roman chamomile, hemp, hops, neroli, valerian, ylang-ylang.

Aggression

There are over 10 types of feline aggression. Remedy selection will be easier if you identify what is making your cat aggressive. The more you know about the 'problem' you are trying to support, the more spot on your remedy selection will be.

For example, for maternal aggression you will need remedies that instill trust and are nurturing, such as linden blossom and rose. If you are dealing with testosterone fueled territory aggression you will need remedies that reduce testosterone such as hops or ylang-ylang.

A herb garden of rose, valerian, hops and calendula is a good place to start if you are unsure which type of aggression you are dealing with. Other Top aromatics for aggression include: Bergamot, hops, jasmine, rose otto, valerian, vetiver.

Change

Cats thrive on routine so any change can upset them, from moving their food station, to moving house. The more happy and relaxed your cat is, the better she will cope with changes. But still, when making changes to your cats environment make them slowly if possible. These remedies can help a cat settle more easily: Cedarwood, geranium, jasmine, neroli, vetiver, violet leaf.

Fear

Fear can express itself in many ways, but usually, a fearful cat will want to hide. If your cat is fearful, make sure she has a place to hide and feel safe. Lack of early socialisation often leads to a fearful cat. The best way you can overcome this fear is to be patient, don't force your attention on the cat, and offer aromatics. Fearful cats can sometimes be aggressive when you approach them, so be cautious and approach slowly. Top aromatics for fear: Angelica root, bergamot, cedarwood, cistus, frankincense, jasmine, linden blossom, valerian.

Inappropriate toileting

If your cat suddenly starts toileting around the house, take them to the vet to check for a urinary infection or other underlying medical issues. Other common reasons for inappropriate urination are too many cats sharing a litter box, or changes in the household that are stressing the cat. This might be a good time to contact a cat behaviourist for further help. But meanwhile offer these remedies: Angelica root, calendula, carrot seed, chamomile, geranium, helichrysum, valerian.

Multi-cat households

In our experience it's rare to find a multi-cat household where the cats all get along. It's more common in multi-cat households that the cats barely tolerate each other, or they don't get along and are aggressive.

One of the biggest issues with multi-cat households is lack of territory. Naturally speaking, cats are solitary hunters and need their own space. If you have many cats make sure they have enough litter trays, high areas, cat beds, and that each one has his/her own territorial area, even if that's just the top of a cupboard. Putting down hydrosols, a few drops in a bowl of water, is a very effective way to calm tensions between cats. Also having regular access to herb gardens allows your cat(s) to take time out, to self-soothe away from any tension or territorial anxiety in the home. You could also offer any of the following: Bergamot, chamomile, clary sage, frankincense, peppermint, rose otto, valerian.

Noise Reactive

When we say 'noise' we mean loud noises such as the hoover or fireworks. Cats are so sensitive with their hearing, but also some cats are naturally timid and cautious, so are affected by loud noises. We would recommend the following: Cedarwood, chamomile, frankincense, hemp, rose buds, valerian, violet leaf.

Old age – mental

Older cats can often become less alert and more confused mentally, which can make them anxious and grumpy. They love having a fresh or dried herb garden to relax with whenever they choose. You can leave it somewhere they always have access to, refreshing the herbs daily. The strong smell of aromatics also seems to help stimulate and focus cats with low-grade dementia, reducing the vocalisation that is common in this situation. Top choices include: Angelica root, bergamot, clary sage, ginger, hemp, lemon balm, spirulina, st johns wort, ylang-ylang.

Overgrooming

This is one of the most common reactive behaviours in cats and it is a sign that your cat needs help. Overgrooming is a self-soothing mechanism that your cat uses to comfort herself to reduce stress, worry and anxiety, indigestion, or pain. It's one of those cases when the remedy selected can help you understand the trigger for the grooming. It's also good to notice where they are licking. Licking the foreleg can be associated with spinal pain, licking the stomach could well be indigestion. Plucking hair, rather than licking is usually anxiety. A note of concern: any form of overgrooming should raise a red flag with you. Take the time to observe your cat, see if you can identify her trigger. Top choices include: Angelica root, carrot seed, cedarwood, chamomile, chickweed, comfrey, jasmine, linden blossom, valerian.

Sadness/loss

A cat can experience loss, sadness or grief just like humans, after all they are sentient beings too. It could be due to the death of a guardian, existing animal in the home or a change of environment. Give your cat time, to process and heal their loss. The following remedies may also support them: Angelica root, neroli, jasmine, helichrysum, linden blossom, yarrow.

As First Aid

Hydrosols, herbal oils and clays can deal with pretty much all your first aid needs, such as stings, scratches, bumps and bruises. Hydrosols can be used to wash wounds, heal bruises and relieve pain, or made into gels to speed healing. They can be antiseptic, antibacterial, anti-inflammatory, relieve pain and aid healthy skin repair. Clay is great for wounds, cuts and sores. It is antifungal, antibacterial, draws out pus and helps the skin to regenerate.

You can also use hydrosols or essential oils in true first response situations while waiting for the vet. We suggest the following hydrosols or essential oils for inhalation:

- Neroli (*Citrus aurantium var bigarade*) for shock
- Helichrysum (*Helichrysum italicum*) for impact injuries
- Yarrow (*Achillea millefolium*) to stop bleeding and relieve trauma.

You could also use lavender (*Lavandula officinalis*) to do any of those things, but it is not quite as powerful. Offering aromatics while waiting for the vet will reduce stress (yours and your cats!) and help speed recovery. For healing minor injuries, you can combine hydrosols, clays and herbal oils, offering hydrosol or diluted essential oil for inhalation and making a topical gel/paste as well. See the recipes on page 60.

Co-operative health care

When healing injuries you can still trust your cat to guide you, even though this is when it's most tempting to force them to take something — anything! — to relieve your worry. Experience (and some very wise cats) have taught us that listening to them is the best option.

If you need to wash a minor wound, offer a choice of hydrosol, such as lavender or helichrysum. Then let them choose between clay or gel to protect it. In a first aid situation you are asking the cat, "Do you strongly object to me using this?" Don't force topical application if your cat resists, but you don't need to see engagement on a deep level, just acceptance.

Allowing your cat a voice in a first aid situation may seem extreme to you, but the truth is when cats are first injured they will generally accept help. As healing progresses, they will start to refuse. The body heals itself given the right conditions, and your cat knows if/when help is needed.

Aromatics rebalance the whole system as well as working directly on wounds, so you can apply them less frequently than a standard antibiotic application. And the really wonderful thing in a first aid situation is, when you have the right aromatic for the occasion your cats don't resist being treated. No more struggling to dress a wound, that's one stress out of the window already!

Essential first aid kit

Hydrosols are the key workers when it comes to 1st aid. They are great for washing wounds and soothing skin. Soak a cotton wool pad in hydrosol and hold it on any traumatic injury. Dilute 50% with filtered water before use.

Hydrosols

- **Helichrysum** antiseptic, anti-bruising, anti-inflammatory
- **Lavender** antiseptic, wound healing, prevents scarring and proud flesh
- **Cornflower** soothing, eye wash
- **Tea tree** antibacterial, dilute with 4 parts water
- **Yarrow** stops bleeding, disinfectant, creates a protective barrier over the wound, anti-inflammatory, releases trauma.

Carrier oils

- **Aloe vera gel** anti-inflammatory, skin soothing
- **Calendula oil** anti-inflammatory, wound healing, antifungal, soothing
- **Nettle oil** stimulates circulation, anti-inflammatory.

Essential oils

- **Valerian** sedative, reduces pain, inhalation only
- **Neroli** for shock, loss of consciousness, inhalation only.

Clay

- Green clay

How To Make
Aromatic Lotions

When to use topicals

We don't use topical application very often with any animals, because healing happens from the inside out. The skin is the largest organ and the safest place for the body to clear toxins. If you re-balance the immune or digestion system, problems such as itchy skin usually clear by themselves. With cats, there are even fewer instances that might call for a topical application. However, skin problems are often the first place that the body lets us know it is out of balance.

When offering for self-selection, you will usually find that the selected remedy will affect both internal and external symptoms. For example, if a cat has been overgrooming due a poor diet they may select chickweed herbal oil. This remedy will soothe the digestive tract and relieve itching from the irritated skin as it re-grows fur.

However, there are some situations that call for external application to help speed recovery and relieve irritation. Or to inhibit a secondary bacterial infection, for instance an abscess.

Anytime an imbalance manifests in the skin you can add the hydrosol your cat chooses to a gel/clay, as well as offering them individually for inhalation or ingestion.

Why we use gels and clays

We use a water-based gel or a clay as the carrier for topical applications. We never use oil-based lotions or creams when working with cats. Apart from the fact that it's going to play havoc with your carpets, water-based gels are easier to make at home. Oil-based lotions can also upset a cats digestion if they lick them off their coat.

Gels and clays are non-toxic and will not harm your cat if she licks them. But you want them to stay on the skin long enough to do their job. If your cat does try to lick straight away, you can offer her the bottle of gel/clay to smell while the gel absorbs, or distract them with a treat!

How to choose between gel and clay?

The first step to making a gel or clay is to offer your cat a couple of appropriate hydrosols to select from. For example, if you are making a wound dressing, you could offer helichrysum, lavender, or tea tree. You could also offer calendula or comfrey macerated oil. Then offer green clay and see how she responds. If she shows interest in the clay, you are going to make a clay, if not, make a gel, as per the instructions below.

How to make a gel or clay

Hydrosol gel
Ingredients:
- 100 ml hydrosol of your/your cats choice,
- 1 teaspoon xanthan or guar gum. This is usually available in health food stores and many aromatherapy suppliers, it's used to thicken the mixture.

Procedure:
Use either a hand mixer or blender to make the gel.
- First, warm the bowl or blender with boiling water This sterilizes the container and makes the hydrosol gel more easily
- Pour hydrosol into the warmed bowl/blender

- Sprinkle the xanthan gum on top of the hydrosol
- Whisk for about 5 minutes or until the xanthan gum has completely dissolved and the gel has thickened
- The gel should be thick enough to hold its shape on your hand when dropped from a teaspoon, but not too thick that it won't spread out slowly. If it feels too "gloopy" add a little more hydrosol, you don't want to end up with a sticky coat.

Apply as needed or when and where your cat guides you.

Clay

Green clay is more often selected when there is a wound or infection. White clay, sprinkled on the skin or made into a very loose lotion can be used to soothe itching. To make a clay, select the hydrosol you want to use, appropriate to your healing intention. In a glass bowl, place 1 tablespoon of clay and stir in hydrosol until it reaches the consistency you want. if you want to draw out an abscess it should be a thick paste. If you want to soothe a rash, it should be like single cream.

Here's a couple of examples of common uses for clays and gels.

Ear wash

If your cat gets "gunky ears", stick to a grain free diet and reduce stress to strengthen the immune system. You can also let your cat select a hydrosol and then make up a gel with hydrosol and a little calendula oil. Soak a cotton ball in the gel and wipe out the ear gently. Hydrosols to offer would include, lavender, helichrysum, thyme or tea tree.

Dental Care

The best way to prevent dental disease is to feed raw meaty bones, appropriate to your cat's size. Feeding a fresh or raw food diet is also much less likely to create an unhealthy build-up of periodontal bacteria. Chewing on fresh grasses will help keep teeth healthy. But there is an epidemic of dental disease in cats, especially those who are immune challenged. If your cat has problems, you can dilute 1 teaspoon of antibacterial hydrosol in 100 ml of water and leave down for your cat to drink if she chooses. If you do need to brush your cat's teeth, don't use essential oils. The most effective and safe natural toothpaste is:

Tooth Powder
- 30 grams white clay
- 5 grams green clay
- An optional 5 grams neem leaf powder, if your cat likes the smell

Dampen a toothbrush or finger and rub the powder into the gums, et voila!

Your Aromatic Pharmacy

What you need to get started

Starting your aromatic collection can seem daunting and expensive at first. But it doesn't have to be. One way to start your collection is to buy the few botanicals you think your cat needs most after reading all about them in the profiles. Then buy more as you need them, slowly building your collection, getting to know each item through hands-on experience and visible results. You don't need an expensive collection to get started. If you have a herb garden and a few of the items from the list below you will be well set.

Here is a list of aromatics that should cover most common eventualities.

General Use Starter Kit

Dried herbs
- Valerian root *(Valeriana officinalis)*
- Catnip leaves *(Nepeta cataria)*
- Rose buds *(Rosa damascena)*
- Calendula flowers *(Calendula officinalis)*
- Yarrow flowers *(Achillea millefolium)*

Hydrosols:
- Carrot seed *(Daucus carota)*
- Lemon Balm *(Melissa officinalis)*
- Neroli *(Citrus aurantium var bigarade)*
- Frankincense *(Boswellia carterii)*
- Lavender *(Lavandula angustifolia)*
- Lemongrass *(Cymbopogon citratus)*
- Roman chamomile *(Anthemis nobilis)*
- Spearmint *(Mentha spicata)*
- Yarrow *(Achillea millefolium)*

Essential oils:
- Bergamot *(Citrus bergamia)*
- Cedarwood *(Cedrus deodara)*
- Vetiver *(Vetiveria zizanoides)*

Carrier oils
- Sunflower *(Helianthus anuus)*
- Calendula *(Calendula officinalis)*
- Hemp *(Cannabis sativa)*

See the Appendix for suppliers in Europe and the US.

Botanical Profiles

Here you will find profiles of some of the plants we use and the preferred form to use with cats: hydrosol, essential oil, dried whole herb, or all of the above.

Angelica Root
(Angelica archangelica)

History and Character

Angelica is a large, graceful plant that can grow to a height of 2 meters/6 ft. The whole plant exudes the energetic depth and reach that gives angelica its healing power. Its roots go deep into the earth and the strong, tall stem "reaches to the heavens" and supports a large white/green umbrella-like flower. The flower can be seen as protective, a place to shelter, as well as open and receptive. The essential oil and hydrosol can be distilled from roots or seeds. We use the root, which is more grounding. The dried root has strong digestive and calmative properties.

Angelica root has been used traditionally to protect against "the Plague", for nervous hysteria, as a general tonic, for "fortifying the spirit", to promote digestion and for female disorders. It strengthens the liver and steadies the heart, improving circulation. Angelica opens the cat up to healing, reconnects them to their inner strength and is said to "connect to the angels." Angelica is innocent and strong at the same time and is very effective where fears or compulsive behaviours have been triggered by a traumatic incident when very young.

Principal Uses

Physical
- Arthritis
- Chronic bronchial disorders
- Circulatory problems
- Cushing's syndrome and other metabolic disorders
- Cats who have shut down due to chronic pain or stress
- Immune stimulant, especially for those run down by a long illness
- Liver dysfunction
- Loss of appetite, including anorexia
- Lymphatic problems
- Stress related digestive disorders

Behavioural
- Chronic anxiety
- Opens the cat up to healing
- Calming, supports emotionally shut down cats
- Overgrooming
- Strengthens the nerves, especially where there is hysteria brought on by nervous exhaustion

Frequently used for:

- Fear or compulsive behaviour, especially after one or more traumatic incidents in early life.
- Old cats who are emotionally hardened or have chronic pain.
- If cats show no interest in any of the other aromatics offered.

Use as: Dried cut root, Hydrosol, Essential oil

Cultivation/Sustainability Mostly cultivated. No known sustainability issues.

Actions: Antifungal, antispasmodic, antitoxic, antibacterial, carminative, digestive, diuretic, expectorant, febrifuge, general tonic, neurotonic.

Safety & Cautions: Non-toxic, non-irritant. Angelica root can be phototoxic when applied to skin. Avoid internal use with diabetes.

Nayana Morag and Julie-Anne Thorne

Bergamot
(Citrus bergamia)

History and Character

Named for the city of Bergamo in northern Italy (Lombardy), this small tree (3.5 meters/12 ft. tall) resembles a miniature orange. Traditionally, it has been used for fever and worms. It is said to kill airborne bacteria and was used to stop the spread of infection in hospitals. One of the main qualities of bergamot is its balancing effect. This is particularly useful when things are out of control, as in growths, tumours and, on an emotional level, moods that swing between extremes. Bergamot's sharp, sweet smell is uplifting and clean, cutting through stagnant energies to release pent up emotions. It has a profound antidepressant effect, especially for those who turn anger and frustration in on themselves, as in self-mutilation or obsessive compulsive behaviour.

Principal Uses

Physical
- Brings bio-system into balance
- Genito-urinary tract infections
- Post parturition
- Tumours, warts, growths of all kinds
- Viral infection

Behavioural
- Depression
- Erratic behaviour
- Anxiety
- Frustrated irritability
- Snappy/intolerant

Frequently used for:

- Warts, growths and tumours, especially if the cat is intolerant or withdrawn.
- Changeable, moody individuals with unpredictable temperament.

Use as: Essential oil

Cultivation/Sustainability: Cultivated. Use organic cultivation.

Actions: Antibacterial, antiseptic, antispasmodic, antiviral, calmative, cicatrizant, febrifuge, parasiticide, sedative, stomachic, tonic, vermifuge.

Safety & Cautions: Whole bergamot oil is phototoxic, so should not be applied to exposed skin up to 12 hours before exposure to ultra-violet. Otherwise it is non-toxic and relatively non-irritant. While it is possible to buy bergapten-free bergamot, we never use it. Because when given the choice cats consistently choose the whole oil over the altered one.

CARROT SEED

(Daucus carota)

History and Character

Wild carrot has a graceful, white flower growing from a succulent root. It is similar to the yellow carrot we know so well, but smaller and paler. The finest carrot seed essential oil is wild harvested in France, where the plant can be found in the fields and hedgerows of rural areas. The oil is well accepted by cats and is nourishing, both physically and emotionally. Carrot seed regenerates liver cells, helps repair damaged skin, rebuilds poor quality coat and nails, and encourages the production of healthy tissue in smooth muscles. This is the oil to use if there is any history of physical or emotional neglect, abandonment or starvation. Because of its connection to nourishment, it is a good oil for loss of appetite for food and life itself. Like a true earth mother, it responds to our needs and helps regenerate the system from the inside out.

Principal Uses

Physical

- Anorexia
- Flatulence
- Heart murmurs
- Liver damage
- Loss of appetite
- Malnutrition (past or present)
- Poor skin and nails
- Slow healing wounds
- Ulcers
- Worms
- Immune support

Behavioural
- Depression
- Emotional neglect or abandonment
- Loss of will to live
- Overgrooming

Frequently used for:
- Past or present, emotional or physical abandonment or neglect.
- Underweight cats, who heal slowly or have poor quality coat.

Use as: Hydrosol, Essential oil

Cultivation/Sustainability: Mostly from cultivated plants. Wild population healthy.

Actions: Anthelmintic, antiseptic, carminative, detoxicant, diuretic, emmenagogue, hepatic, regenerative, smooth muscle relaxant, stimulant, tonic, vasodilator.

Safety & Cautions: Generally non-toxic, non-sensitizing. Can be harsh on skin and mucous membranes, dilute well.

CALENDULA
(Calendula officinalis)

History and Character

Calendula, also known as marigold, is a cheerful presence in gardens across the globe. It grows easily in any soil and is used as a companion plant as it helps keep vegetables free from pests. The double orange flowers, harvested on warm days, are the best ones for macerating. The oil takes on their beautiful golden colour.

Calendula is a valuable healer, and as there is no distilled essential oil (there is a CO2 extract), the macerated oil is particularly useful. We use calendula often as a carrier oil, food supplement for stomach and fungal skin problems, and for wiping out "gunky" ears. Emotionally it is uplifting and comforting, good for depression and self-confidence. Great to have on a herb garden mat.

Tagetes glandulifera is also known as marigold, but is not safe to use. Be sure to check the full Latin name when purchasing.

Principle uses

Physical
- Bruises and capillary damage
- Dry, cracked skin
- Fungal infections
- Slow healing wounds
- Gall bladder complaints
- Hormonal problems
- Indigestion
- Ulcers

Behavioural
- Helps to boost self-confidence and self-esteem
- Good for nervous or timid cats

Frequently used for:

- Multi-cat households.
- Cats that overgroom, especially if the lack self-confidence or frequently vomit.
- Wound healing.

Use as: Dried flower heads and petals, Herbal oil, Essential Oil

Cultivation/Sustainability: From cultivated plants.

Actions: Anthelmintic, antiseptic, carminative, detoxicant, diuretic, emmenagogue, hepatic, regenerative, smooth muscle relaxant, stimulant, tonic, vasodilator.

Safety & Cautions: No known contraindications. Do not confuse with *Tagetes* varieties.

CATNIP
(Nepeta cataria)

History and Character

Catnip can also be called catswort, and catmint. Catnip is a member of the Lamiaceae family, to which peppermint also belongs. It is one of the most common botanicals associated with cats, however not all cats are affected by it. Only two thirds of cats are affected by the primary component nepetalactone. So, don't be surprised if your cat doesn't select it!

Nepeta cataria is a short-lived perennial, that grows to be 50–100 cm (20–40 in) tall and wide. It blooms from late spring through autumn. The leaves look similar to that of peppermint in their almost diamond shape. The small, flowers are fragrant and usually pink in color. Cats are usually attracted to the leaves rather than the flowers, you can offer it fresh or high quality dried. Catnip seeds are easy to get hold of and grow, so you can grow your own indoors, or on a balcony to add enrichment for your cat.

When catnip is inhaled it produces a stimulating effect, yet when ingested it sedates. It is a great remedy to offer daily as it helps the cat emotionally and aids digestion. You may see your cat rub, roll, lick or chew catnip and then have a crazy 5 minutes but this will soon wear off, leaving them with a happy, feel-good effect.

Principle uses

Physical
- Stomach upsets
- Digestion issues

Behavioural
- Restless, anxious, stressed cats
- Cats who are closed down

Frequently used for:

- Enrichment for all cats – good for multi-cat households.
- Cats that have withdrawn, especially if they have stomach upsets.
- Cats that need to have a little fun.

Use as: Dry/fresh leaf, Macerated oil, Essential oil

Cultivation/Sustainability: Use organic, high quality where possible. No known sustainability concerns.

Actions: Calmative, nervine, sedative, smooth muscle relaxant, soothing, soporific, stimulant, stomachic.

Safety & Cautions: Cats may become temporarily aggressive when working with catnip – this is an unusual response and could be due to an energy shift. Give the cat the opportunity to have space and process the situation.

Nayana Morag and Julie-Anne Thorne

CEDARWOOD HIMALAYAN
(Cedrus deodara)

History and Character

This magnificent tree is graceful and powerful with an awesome presence. It is found abundantly throughout the Himalayan region where it is known as the "House of God".

Cedarwood has a long tradition of religious use in various cultures, as an incense and for building temples. The Egyptians used it for cosmetics and embalming. The cedar tree grows in the high mountains, where the air is clean and fresh. The tree has deep spreading roots and a tall straight trunk. The branches are flexible, moving in the wind but anchored to the central trunk, so it gives a "quiet center when all around is moving" Cedarwood oil grounds and centers cats in their being, helping them to take a deep breath so they can face up to tough situations. It helps those who feel alienated, or fear that they don't have the strength to "hold it together", or generally feel overwhelmed by circumstances over which they have no control over.

Cedarwood gives inner calm in times of instability and is one of the oils to try if you are moving house or making similar major life changes.

Principal Uses

Physical
- Asthma
- Catarrh
- Hair loss
- Insect repellent
- Edema

- Weak kidneys or back
- Wheezing

Behavioural
- Fear, timidity
- Lack of willpower
- New home or moving house
- Overgrooming

Frequently used for:

- Those who are unsettled by their surroundings or have just moved home.
- Timid fearful cat cats, especially if there is a history of back-ache, kidney problems or hair loss.

Use as: Hydrosol, Essential oil

Cultivation/Sustainability: Of least concern, mostly harvested from wild forests, unlike *Cedrus Atlantica* which is vulnerable.

Actions: Anticatarrhal, antiparasitic, antirheumatic, anti-seborrhea, cicatrizant, diuretic, expectorant, general tonic, lymphatic decongestant.

Safety & Cautions: Non-toxic and non-irritant in prescribed doses.

Nayana Morag and Julie-Anne Thorne

CHAMOMILE, GERMAN
(Matricaria recutita)

History and Character

German chamomile grows up to 60 cm (2') tall, with a branching stem bearing sprays of small white flowers with a pale yellow center. It is similar in action to Roman chamomile, but more powerfully anti-inflammatory and anti-allergenic, it is one of the most anti-inflammatory essential oils. It also soothes irritated skin.

Emotionally, German chamomile soothes anxiety and is useful for those who tend to express their emotions through their body, getting ill rather than getting upset. German chamomile is especially good for cats who are stoic and don't show their feelings easily. One of this oil's most useful actions is its ability to unblock the flow of energy in the body, so there is often a squishy or stodgy feel or look to cats who need German chamomile. The deep blue colour of this oil is due to the chamazulene, which is an anti-inflammatory agent and an outcome of the distillation process.

Principal Uses

Physical
- Eruptive skin conditions
- Insect bites
- Allergies effecting skin or lungs
- Arthritis
- Soft tissue swellings
- Spasmodic colic
- Ulcers
- Fungal infection

Behavioural
- Anxiety
- Irritability
- Impatience

Frequently used for:
- Allergic skin reactions especially if the cat is worn down and irritable.
- Anxious cats that are hiding or appear withdrawn.
- Fungal infections.

Use as: Dry/fresh flowers, Hydrosol, Essential oil

Cultivation/Sustainability: Use organic where possible. No known sustainability concerns.

Actions: Analgesic, anti-allergenic, antifungal, anti-inflammatory, antispasmodic, bactericidal, digestive, emmenagogue, hepatic, nerve sedative, stimulates leucocyte production, vulnerary.

Safety & Cautions: Generally held to be non-toxic and non-irritant. Can cause contact dermatitis in some individuals.

CHAMOMILE, ROMAN
(Anthemis nobilis, Chamamaelum nobile)

History and Character

Roman Chamomile is a small, half spreading herb with feathery leaves and daisy like flowers. A sweet and gentle plant, delicate yet sturdy. Native to southern and western Europe, it is widely cultivated throughout Europe and the United States.

This pale blue oil, is similar to its cousin German chamomile, but less anti-inflammatory and more suited to those who are likely to make a fuss about every little thing, rather than "man up" and bear it stoically. Roman chamomile is ideal for those who are constitutionally nervous, "jumping out of their skins" and over reactive, especially if suffering from diarrhoea when anxious.

The oil calms the nerves, stomach and skin, and helps them live more comfortably in their skins, physically and emotionally. It is "the child's oil", as it is gentle, soothing and works well for "growing up" problems, such as teething, colic and restlessness. It also helps cats who are fearful or nervous with children and soothes immature tantrums and outbursts of emotion.

Principal Uses

Physical
- Diarrhoea
- Eczema
- Inflamed, itchy skin
- Nervous digestive problems
- Stress related skin problems

Behavioural
- Constitutional nervousness
- Anxiety manifesting in the stomach

- Fear, nervousness or intolerance of children
- Nervous aggression
- Obsessive worry
- Restlessness

Frequently used for:

- Nervous flighty cats, especially if they suffer from itchy, irritable skin, or stress related upset stomachs.
- Any issues involving children, and frustration or angry outbursts.

Use as: Dry/fresh flowers, Hydrosol, Essential oil

Cultivation/Sustainability: Use organic where possible. No known sustainability concerns.

Actions: Analgesic, anti-inflammatory, anti-neuralgic, antiparasitic, antiseptic, antispasmodic, carminative, digestive, sedative, tonic, vulnerary.

Safety & Cautions: Generally non-toxic and non-irritant. It can cause dermatitis in some individuals.

CHICKWEED

(Stellaria media)

History and Character

Chickweed is considered a weed in most gardens, but the healing properties of this plant are wondrous. The plant likes rich soil and is easy to grow all year round in temperate climates. The bright green, pointed, oval leaves appear along a long thin length, the tiny white shaped flowers only blossom for a day or two. It is sometimes called common chickweed to distinguish it from other plants called chickweed, and other names include: chickenwort, craches, maruns or winterweed. It is cultivated for both human and poultry consumption.

Japanese will often add the petals to a cooling, summer salad. In the 17th century herbalist John Gerard recommended it as a remedy for mange. Modern herbalists prescribe it for iron-deficiency anemia (for its high iron content), as well as for skin diseases, bronchitis, rheumatic pains and arthritis. We use chickweed for its cooling effect on the body, both internally and externally, and to aid digestion.

Principle uses

Physical
- Hairballs
- Constipation
- Itchy skin
- Digestive tract inflammation

Behavioural
- Overgrooming
- Anxiety manifesting in the digestive system
- Picky with food – reluctance to eat

Frequently used for:

- Cats who are having troubles eating or need support to soothe their throat, tummy and colon. Especially if they are over-grooming.

Use as: Dry/fresh leaf, Macerated oil

Cultivation/Sustainability: No known sustainability concerns.

Actions: Antacid, anti-pruritic, carminative, digestive stimulant, digestive tonic, soothing, stomachic.

Safety & Cautions: Chickweed contains saponins, which can be toxic when consumed in extremely large quantities.

CLARY SAGE
(Salvia sclarea)

History and Character

Clary sage is a sturdy perennial herb with hairy, pale green, purple tinged leaves and insignificant blue flowers. Native to southern Europe it is also cultivated worldwide wherever the soil is well drained. In the Middle Ages it was known as Cleareye, which refers both to its ability to cleanse the eyes (the herb, not the essential oil) and its reputation for inducing visions.

It is closely related to garden sage (*Salvia officinalis*), but since it has lower levels of ketones is much safer to use. Clary sage is known as a euphoric and is deeply relaxing for muscles and mind. It is grounding, earthy and inspiring. It is said to have a progesterone like effect and can be used to regulate hormonal cycles. It also helps to release energy in the lower chakras and encourages sexual activity. Last but not least, Clary sage releases constriction in the lungs, deepening breathing and relieving fearful tension.

Principal Uses

Physical
- Alopecia
- Asthma
- Circulatory problems
- Claustrophobia
- Hormonal problems
- Tight or strained muscles

Behavioural
- Anxiety
- Changeable moods
- Claustrophobia

- Depression
- Fear

Frequently used for:

- Restless, moody cats, especially if there is any constriction of lungs or muscles, or claustrophobia.
- Bad tempered females, especially if they are defensive of their personal space, or become moody or uncomfortable around their hormonal cycle.

Use as: Hydrosol, Essential oil

Cultivation/Sustainability: No known concerns.

Actions: Antifungal, antiseptic, antispasmodic, antisudorific, detoxicant, decongestant, hormone balancer (progesterone-like), neurotonic, phlebotonic, regenerative.

Safety & Cautions: Non–toxic, non-irritant, non-sensitizing.

Cistus
(Cistus ladanifer)

History and Character

Cistus ladanifer is a species of flowering plant in the family Cistaceae. It is native to the western Mediterranean region, being particularly prolific in Portugal and Spain, where it has taken over much of what was once farmland and grasslands in the mountain regions. The leaves are evergreen and lanceolate, dark green above and paler underneath. The flowers have 5 papery white petals, usually with a red to maroon spot at the base, surrounding the yellow stamens and pistils. The whole plant is covered with sticky, fragrant resin. The plant is known as a pioneer species, moving into repair land that has been degraded, especially if it is cracked and dry.

It is a sturdy shrub, flourishing in harsh environments, yet bears a profusion of delicate white flowers that bloom and fade quickly, thus it symbolises both softness, transience and endurance.

Cistus is one of the plants known as Rose of Sharon, and is possibly the burning bush in the biblical story of Moses. The essential oil is steam distilled from the twigs and leaves and is one of the best skin healing agents, reducing scarring. The hydrosol soothes itchy skin, especially if dry and cracked.

Cistus helps cats who have shut themselves off and become emotionally cold, due to past trauma. The cistus type can seem self-reliant and finds it hard to trust others, but at the same time they struggle to contain their emotions, and over-respond to stimuli. We have found it clears deeply held generational trauma, particularly any trauma from fires or burning.

Principal uses

Physical
- Adrenal exhaustion
- Arthritis
- Catarrhal coughs
- Immune modulated diseases
- Nervous diarrhoea
- Nervous exhaustion
- Scars
- Wheezing
- Wounds

Behavioural
- After any traumatic incident to clear the nervous system
- Emotional detachment
- Congenital fear
- Lack of self-expression
- Nervousness
- Over-submissive
- Restlessness

Frequently used for:
- Older cats with chronic skin problems, especially if they are emotionally cold or detached, or suffer from the cold,
- Cats who over-respond emotionally, especially if they have respiratory problems, or a history of past abuse or trauma, particularly anything involving fire.

Use as: Hydrosol, Essential oil

Cultivation/Sustainability: Wildcrafted. Healthy, wild, population, considered a weed.

Actions: Antiseptic, anti-infectious, anti-microbial, antiviral, bactericidal, anti-inflammatory, antitussive, astringent, calming, cicatrisant, mucolytic, styptic, tonic for the nervous system, vulnerary.

Safety & Cautions: No known cautions.

COMFREY
(Symphytum officinale)

History and Character

Comfrey's large hairy leaves and delicate purplish pink flowers are a common sight throughout Europe, but especially in the British Isles. The macerated oil can be made from the roots or leaves of this sturdy plant, or both. Comfrey is a well known healer's plant, having been used extensively in herbal medicine. One of its common names is Knitbone due to its ability to speed the healing of broken bones, bruises and wounds. It was also traditionally used for irritable coughs and chronic lung conditions.

Principle uses

Physical
- Broken bones
- Scar tissue and proud flesh
- Strengthens the lungs
- Traumatic injury
- Pain and inflammation
- Muscular aches
- Degenerative joints
- Wounds

Frequently used for:
- Older cats suffering with joint pain.
- Cats recovering from an operation or medical treatment or any traumatic injury.

Use as: Dried leaf, Macerated oil

Cultivation/Sustainability: No known sustainability concerns.

Actions: Anti-inflammatory, demulcent, expectorant, pulmonary, vulnerary.

Safety & Cautions: Do not use on puncture wounds or other very deep wounds. Over consumption of the root has caused cancer in mice.

Fennel, Sweet

(Foeniculum vulgare var. dulce)

History and Character

Fennel is a hardy perennial or biennial herb with soft, green, ferny leaves and umbrels of yellow flowers. Native to the shores of the Mediterranean it is now widely cultivated. Aromatherapy uses Sweet or garden fennel, not bitter or common fennel, which has a high level of the potentially harmful ketone, fenchone.

Traditionally, fennel has been used as a culinary herb worldwide. The Ancient Greeks used it as a diuretic to help lose weight and to promote strength. In Europe, fennel was hung over cottage doors as protection against witchcraft. It was known as an antidote for all sorts of poisons and snakes were said to rub against it to improve their eyesight. Perhaps due to its anti-toxic properties, fennel was said to provide courage, strength and longevity.

It is a warm, dry oil that has great affinity with the female reproductive system and the energy of nurture and care. Since it is helpful in finding ways of expressing a caring nature constructively, it is good for those who think too much, worry about the welfare of others, or have an obsessive need to nurture (sometimes manifesting as phantom pregnancy). It also helps release gas and bloating in the digestive system, and generally relieves damp, which can lead to fatty lumps and edema.

Principal Uses

Physical

- Arthritis, rheumatism
- Constipation
- Fatty lumps
- Fluid retention

- Intestinal gas
- Phantom pregnancy
- Poisonous bites
- Problems with lactation
- To regulate hormonal cycles
- Urinary infections

Behavioural
- Anxiety related obsessive behaviour
- Over/under active nurture impulses
- Those who worry about others or seek constant reassurance

Frequently used for:

- Emotionally insecure cats who are over concerned with others, especially if there is a history of digestive upsets, flatulence, hormonal imbalance or fluid retention.
- Obsessive anxiety.
- Tumours and soft lumps, especially mammary.

Use as: Hydrosol, Essential oil

Cultivation/Sustainability: No known sustainability concerns.

Actions: Analgesic, antibacterial, antifungal, anti-inflammatory, antiseptic, antispasmodic, cardiotonic, carminative, cholagogic, circulatory stimulant, decongestant, digestive, diuretic, emmenagogic, hormone-like, lactogenic, laxative, litholytic, oestrogen like, respiratory tonic (rapid breathing).

Safety & Cautions: Generally considered to be non-sensitizing. Use only in high dilutions. Do not use during pregnancy.

FRANKINCENSE
(Boswellia carterii)

History and Character

Frankincense is a small tree or shrub with masses of pinnate leaves and white or pale pink flowers. It grows wild throughout the deserts of Northeast Africa. It has been an important incense in all the religions of the world since the ancient Egyptians. Frankincense slows and deepens breathing, which is why it is useful for asthma.

It is also said to "distance the mind from worries and fears". Frankincense eases the passage through major transitions, including death, and can be offered to cats approaching the end. Frankincense also helps to let go of the past and old attachments that have outgrown their usefulness. It calms and centers the mind, allowing cats to focus on the present.

Principal Uses

Physical
- Asthma
- Claustrophobia
- Diarrhoea, especially if triggered by nerves
- Dry, sensitive skin
- Scars, ulcers and wounds
- Skin growths
- To ease the passage into death

Behavioural
- Anxiety and restlessness
- Noise sensitivity
- Specific fears such as fireworks or strangers

Frequently used for:

- Anxious or fearful cats, especially if they have asthma, or loose stools.
- Fear of fireworks, loud noises and other known triggers.
- When considering euthanasia.

Use as: Hydrosol, Essential Oil

Cultivation/Sustainability: Wildcrafted. Near threatened status, very important to find sustainable sources when buying.

Actions: Analgesic, anticatarrhal, antidepressive, anti-inflammatory, antiseptic, antioxidant, cicatrizant, energizing, expectorant, immunostimulant.

Safety & Cautions: Generally held to be non-toxic, non-irritant and non-sensitizing but can be harsh on skin and mucous membranes.

GERANIUM
(Pelargonium graveolens)

History and Character

A sprawling, aromatic perennial shrub with hairy serrated leaves and small pink flowers. Pelargonium graveolens is native to South Africa but widely cultivated. Until recently, the essential oil was mostly produced in Réunion (Bourbon), Egypt, Madagascar and China, with the Bourbon oil being the most prized. South Africa now produces a very good quality oil as well.

Since there is so much confusion between pelargonium, which we call geranium, and true geranium, which we call cranesbill or herb Robert, it is not clear what the historical uses of the plant were. Nevertheless, the strongest physical and energetic action of geranium oil is "to regulate". This is due to its powerful effect on the adrenal cortex, which regulates hormones and other endocrine functions.

It is one of the most Yin of the essential oils and helps cats to reconnect with the feminine principle, increasing sensitivity, spontaneity, and the ability to receive. And making cats feel secure in themselves. Geranium can be used anywhere there is a lack of Yin, which is characterized by dryness, rigidity, or overheating, and is especially good for mature females.

Principal Uses

Physical
- All endocrine imbalances
- Dry or greasy flaky skin
- Facial neuralgia
- Fungal infections of the skin
- Hormone problems

- Lice and mosquitoes
- Skin problems, especially greasy dandruff

Behavioural
- Insecure, moody types
- New home or other disruptions to lifestyle
- Balances the mind and body
- Relieves emotional/physical stagnation of energy

Frequently used for:

- Insecure or depressed cats who lack self-confidence, especially if their moods are cyclical or their skin is over dry, greasy or unbalanced.
- Older females/adolescent males who show a lack of receptivity.

Use as: Fresh herb, Hydrosol, Essential oil

Cultivation/Sustainability: Cultivated.

Actions: Analgesic, antibacterial, antidiabetic, antifungal, anti-inflammatory, antiseptic, antispasmodic, astringent, cicatrizant, decongestant, digestive, hemostatic, insect repellent, phlebotonic (lymph) relaxant, tonic to liver and kidneys.

Safety & Cautions: Generally held to be non-toxic, non-irritant and non-sensitizing. It has been known to trigger dermatitis in some individuals, especially with the Bourbon type.

GINGER

(Zingiber officinale)

History and Character

An erect, reed like perennial herb growing from a spreading tuberous pungent rhizome. Native to southern Asia but widely cultivated throughout the tropics. Ginger is a well-known cooking spice and healing remedy that has been used for thousands of years. Best known as a digestive, it is also used for nausea and travel sickness.

Ginger is useful for overproduction of mucous, or diarrhoea. Due to its deeply warming nature, ginger is often appreciated by older cats and those who suffer from arthritis. Energetically, ginger is hot and stimulant and a restorative of Yang energy, giving a boost to those who lack physical energy. Ginger ignites those who lack confidence and the determination to carry things through, increases feelings of self-worth, and lifts the despondent.

Principal Uses

Physical
- Arthritis
- Backache
- Congested lungs and sinus (white or clear mucous)
- Diarrhoea
- Flatulence
- Lack of sexual performance
- Muscular aches and pains
- Pancreatic problems
- Sluggish digestion
- Soft lumps on skin
- Travel sickness

Nayana Morag and Julie-Anne Thorne

Behavioural
- Depression
- Lack of confidence
- Good for withdrawn cats

Frequently used for:
- Depressed, run down cats, especially if they have non-specific skin nodules, diarrhoea or clear mucous.
- Cats that need a 'pick me up' either physically or emotionally.

Use as: Hydrosol, Essential oil

Cultivation/Sustainability: Cultivated, use organic.

Actions: Analgesic, anticatarrhal, carminative, digestive, expectorant, general tonic, sexual tonic, stomachic.

Safety & Cautions: Generally held to be non-toxic, non-irritant, but long-term use can cause sensitization. Dilute well.

HELICHRYSUM
(Helichrysum italicum)

History and Character

A strongly aromatic shrub, about 60 cm./2 ft. tall with a multi branched stem of silvery, lanceolate leaves, helichrysum is native to the Mediterranean region (especially the eastern part). The small, bright yellow, daisy like flowers dry out as the plant matures, but still retain their color and fragrance. Hence the common name of Everlast or *immortelle*.

Traditionally used in a decoction for migraine, chronic respiratory problems, liver ailments and all types of skin conditions, this is the best essential oil for bruises. What's more, unlike the other famous bruise remedy, arnica, it can be used on broken skin to disinfect cuts.

Helichrysum has a similar effect on bruised emotions, dissolving resentment held over from past injuries. Energetically, helichrysum releases blocked energy, especially anger that has been repressed and become resentful.

Principal Uses

Physical
- Aches, pains, strains
- Allergies
- Asthma, bronchitis, chronic coughs
- Bacterial infections
- Bruises and wounds
- Burns, boils, eczema
- Hepatic congestion
- Nervous exhaustion

Behavioural
- Deeply hurt emotions
- Habitually negative behaviour
- Past abuse
- Resentful, simmering anger

Frequently used for:

- Cats holding resentment over past abuse, so stuck in negative patterns that are counter productive. Especially if they have irritated skin.
- Any bumps/bruises, impact injury, rash, or burn.

Use as: Dried flowers, Hydrosol, Essential oil

Cultivation/Sustainability: No known sustainability concerns.

Actions: Anti-allergenic, anticatarrhal, anticoagulant, antidiabetic, antifungal, antihaematomic, anti-inflammatory, antiseptic, antispasmodic, antiviral, digestive, cholagogic, cicatrizant, hepatic, mucolytic, neurotonic, phlebotonic, stimulant.

Safety & Cautions: Generally held to be non-toxic, non-irritant and non-sensitizing.

Hemp

(Cannabis sativa)

History and Character

Hemp seed oil is extracted from the seeds of the controversial cannabis plant. While the oil does not contain the psychoactive properties of the drug, it is, nevertheless, relaxing, warming and comforting. It has a strong nutty flavor, a high gamma linoleic acid (GLA) content and is nutritionally high in protein. The same plant is used for making a strong, pliable material or rope and hemp seed oil is a great carrier oil for cats who are having a hard time "holding it together", physically or emotionally.

Principle uses

Physical
- Arthritis/mobility issues
- Degenerative diseases
- Dry skin
- Eczema
- General weakness
- Digestive issues

Behavioural
- Anxiety
- Nervousness

NB: Hemp is really effective when used in conjunction with valerian and hops.

Frequently used for:

- Anxious cats in a new environment, especially if they are stiff or weak.
- Multi-cat households.

Use as: Cold pressed oil, Essential oil

Cultivation/Sustainability: Cultivated, buy organic.

Actions: Analgesic, anxiolytic, anticonvulsant, antiemetic, antispasmodic, antitussive, cicatrisant, muscle relaxant, possibly hormonal adaptogen, soporific.

Safety & Cautions: None known.

Hops

(Humulus lupulus)

History and character

Hops are the flowers (also called seed cones or strobiles) of the hop plant Humulus lupulus, a member of the Cannabaceae family of flowering plants. They are used primarily as a bitter flavouring and stability agent in beer, and other drinks. The hops vine is a vigorous, climbing perennial usually trained to grow up canes and string in cultivated fields. Hops originated in northern Eurasia, but is now widely cultivated throughout the world, mostly for flavouring beer. Historically hops were known for their effect on oestrogen. Hops can be quite bitter if ingested.

Medicinally hops is known for its sedative and soothing effects, often used with anxious and nervous cats. It helps to support cats who are displaying aggression due to testosterone.

Principal uses

Physical
- Estrogen support
- Sexual excitability

Behavioural
- Anxiety
- Aggression
- Hyper-activity
- Nervousness
- Restlessness

NB: Hops is really effective when used in conjunction with valerian and hemp.

Nayana Morag and Julie-Anne Thorne

Frequently used for:

- Male cats, whether entire or neutered who show aggressive behaviours.
- Multi-cat households with aggression.

Use as: Dried flowers, Essential oil

Cultivation/Sustainability: Cultivated. No known sustainability concerns.

Actions: Anti-anemic, antiseptic, fortifying, hepatic, immune tonic, immunostimulant, kidney tonic, regenerative, restorative, soothing, stomachic.

Safety & Cautions: None known.

JASMINE
(Jasminum officinale)

History and Character

The star-shaped, waxy jasmine flower grows on an evergreen vine or shrub. It is native to China, northern India and west Asia and there are many varieties. The fragrance of jasmine is considered to be one of the most sensually evocative and is strongest after dark and just before dawn, which is when the flowers are harvested for oil production. Because the flowers are so delicate they must be harvested by hand, yielding only a little essential oil which is processed through solvent extraction to create and absolute.

For this reason, jasmine is an expensive item, but is indispensable in its role as a Yang balancer. Traditionally jasmine was known as a fertility herb and has been used as an aphrodisiac and to facilitate birth. It is a warming, euphoric oil that instils optimism, eases nervous anxiety, and soothes restlessness. In aromatherapy, it is known as 'King of oils' as, despite its sweet, floral top-note, it has a particular affinity with male hormonal and excess Yang behaviours, especially for males who act 'macho' to hide insecurity. We have found it to be a really nurturing and supportive remedy for cats.

Principal Uses

Physical
- Infertility
- Impotence

Behavioural
- Sexual anxiety
- Nervous anxiety
- Headstrong
- Bullying

Nayana Morag and Julie-Anne Thorne

- Dominant behaviours
- Stressed/withdrawn
- Insecurity
- Overgrooming
- Excess 'Yang' behaviour

Frequently used for:

- Bullying or other hierarchy issues, especially if the cat has been left in a position of responsibility that it does not feel up to, and is nervous when separated from others.
- Cats who want to take charge in a forceful manner because they are actually insecure.
- Cats who are feeling neglected, or need nurturing or comforting.

Use as: Dried flowers, Essential oil

Cultivation/Sustainability: Cultivated.

Actions: Analgesic, antidepressant, calmative, carminative, cicatrisant, emollient, sexual tonic, uterine tonic.

Safety & Cautions: Generally held to be non-toxic, non-irritant and non-sensitising. Allergic reactions have been seen in some individuals. It is sometimes contaminated with the solvent hexane, used to separate the absolute from the concrete.

Juniper Berry

(Juniperus communis)

History and Character

A shrubby, evergreen tree with bluish green needles, small flowers and green or black berries, juniper is found throughout the northern hemisphere. There are several species of juniper from which an oil is produced, and their actions are different. So pay attention to the full Latin name.

Traditionally, juniper berry has been used for urinary infections, respiratory problems and gastrointestinal conditions. It also flushes out the liver and breaks down uric acid. Juniper's sharp pungent fragrance dispels negativity and since ancient times has been used for spiritual purification.

It is especially powerful with clearing out and protecting psychic space. Juniper berry benefits cats who are overwhelmed by crowds, or lack confidence in social groups, and helps to settle cats who feel restless after being at "an occasion" such as a social gathering or show.

Principal Uses

Physical
- After medical procedures to cleanse the liver
- Arthritis
- Kidney infections
- Fluid retention
- Muscle cramps
- Edema
- Overworked soft tissue

Nayana Morag and Julie-Anne Thorne

Behavioural
- Nervous snappishness
- Restlessness
- Suspicion
- Those who are restless in or overwhelmed by crowds
- Trying to please
- Emotional neglect
- Lack of self-worth

Frequently used for:

- Cats who have withdrawn into themselves, often being grumpy and actively protective of their space. Especially if there is any stiffness of joints or muscles, weakening of the bladder, or a history of medical procedures requiring anesthetic.
- Cats who are fearful of humans, or crowds in the home.

Use as: Hydrosol, Essential oil

Cultivation/Sustainability: No known concerns.

Actions: Analgesic, anti-diabetic, antiseptic, detoxicant, digestive tonic, diuretic, hypo-uremic (breaks down uric acid), litholytic, soporific.

Safety & Cautions: Generally held to be non-toxic, non-irritant and non-sensitizing. It should be used with caution in patients with kidney inflammation as high levels of the diuretics 4-terpineol and terpinen-4-ol may cause irritation. Do not use in pregnancy.

LAVENDER
(Lavandula angustifolia/officinalis)

History and Character

An evergreen perennial herb with pale spiky leaves and violet blue flowers that rise above the main bush on slender stalks. Native to the Mediterranean but now cultivated all over the world, the best oil traditionally comes from Provence (France).

Many countries now produce good quality lavender, and it is worth having a selection as each lavender carries the energy of the land and culture producing it. For example, lavender from England is genteel, moist and very soothing. Lavender from Israel is hot, dry and very fast acting. Lavender grown at high altitude is the most energetically refined. Because of its popularity lavender is frequently adulterated with synthetic linalool, so always buy from suppliers who sell to therapists.

Lavender has been with us as a folk remedy for a very long time and is intimately interwoven with the development of aromatherapy as it is known today. Lavender is said to have a highly synergistic nature, strengthening the actions of other oils it is blended with. Energetically, lavender is cool and dry, soothing our brows in times of feverish emotions. It stills the heart and helps oversensitive cats express themselves. It is particularly useful for those whose emotions overwhelm reason, paralyzing action or inducing hysteria.

Principal Uses

Physical
- Burns
- Flea repellent
- Proud flesh
- Scars

- Sinusitis
- Stress related skin conditions
- Swellings
- To support other oils
- Wounds

Behavioural
- Nervous hysteria
- Shock
- Shyness
- Anxiety

Frequently used for:

- All types of skin conditions, especially if cats show nervous restlessness and/or have a strong need for connection.
- Shy, timid cats who want to connect but don't dare.
- Multi-cat households.

Use as: Dry/fresh flower heads, Hydrosol, Essential oil

Cultivation/Sustainability: No known concerns. Use organic.

Actions: Analgesic, antibacterial, antifungal, anti-inflammatory, antiseptic, antispasmodic, calmative, cardiotonic, carminative, cicatrizant, emmenagogic, hypotensive, sedative, tonic.

Safety & Cautions: Generally held to be non-toxic, non-irritant and non-sensitizing. However, lavender essential oil is often adulterated and is classified as a skin irritant.

LEMONGRASS
(Cymbopogon citratus)

History and Character

Lemongrass is a fast growing tropical grass, with long sharp leaves and a thick network of roots. It has an invigorating, sharp, lemony scent, with a grassy, rooty undertone. Due to its fragrance and antiseptic properties lemongrass is commonly used in soaps and cleaning products.

In India it is also widely used in Ayurvedic medicine to: help bring down fevers; treat infectious illnesses; as a tea to calm stomach cramps; and as a pesticide and preservative for palm leaf manuscripts. Lemongrass has also traditionally been used for arthritis and muscular pain.

In 2006 researchers at Israel's University of Ben Gurion found that lemongrass caused apoptosis (programmed cell death) in cancer cells in vitro. This oil is both stimulant and sedative, clearing the mind, grounding the body and relieving anxiety.

Principal uses

Physical
- Diarrhoea
- Digestive upset
- Flea and mosquito repellent
- Fungal infection
- Lymphatic drainage
- Nervous exhaustion
- Neuralgia
- Rheumatism
- Soft tissue damage
- Tumours
- Viral infections

Nayana Morag and Julie-Anne Thorne

Behavioural
- Anxiety
- Confusion
- Depression

Frequently used for:
- In flea or fly spray, especially for cats who tend to be stiff.
- Chronic problems of the digestive or musculo-skeletal system, especially if accompanied by depression or anxiety.

Use as: Fresh grass, Hydrosol, Essential Oil

Cultivation/Sustainability: No known concerns.

Actions: Analgesic, antidepressant, antimicrobial, antiseptic, antispasmodic, astringent, anti-tumor fungicidal, insecticidal, nervine, sedative (nervous system).

Safety & Cautions: While generally held to be non-toxic, there are possibilities of adverse reactions on skin, therefore use at low dilutions.

Linden Blossom
(Tilia cordata)

History and character

Tilia cordata is one of many forms of Linden. Tilia is a genus of approximately 30 species of trees native to the northern hemisphere. Their size can range from fifty to one hundred feet. Tilia is a deciduous, cone-shaped tree often used to line city streets, Tilia blooms in early summer and has pale yellow or cream gently aromatic flowers. There are several trees commonly known as Linden. We refer to Tilia cordata which is also known as little leaf linden and small-leaved linden, so it's important to check Latin name when purchasing.

Linden blossom is a common domestic remedy in Europe, often used to promote a restful night's sleep. The leaves, flowers, and buds are used, and their properties may be regarded as calming and anxiolytic. Traditionally it has been used for restlessness, nasal congestions, painful and difficult digestion, and mild hysteria. For cats it is frequently selected for issues of trust. A word of warning, cats may hiss or react aggressively initially, as they release blocked emotion, but should settle after the initial outburst. Give the cat time to process and relax.

Principal uses

Physical
- Digestion
- heart palpitations
- Rheumatism
- Nasal congestion

Behavioural
- Lack of trust
- Fearful
- Anxious
- Physical/emotional abuse
- Introverted
- Overgrooming
- Reactive (fear aggression)
- Restless

Frequently used for:

- Nervous, anxious and withdrawn cats, especially in a new environment.
- Cats with a lack of trust and fear of specific things.
- Behaviour modification – such as grooming.

Use as: Dried flowers, Hydrosol Absolute

Cultivation/Sustainability: No known concerns.

Actions: Calmative, soothing, sedative, antispasmodic, diaphoretic anxiolytic, decongestant, hypotensive.

Safety & Cautions: Possible interaction with other anxiolytic medication.

Lemon Balm
(Melissa officinalis)

History and Character

This plant originated in the Mediterranean region but is now widely cultivated. It is a leafy perennial, with small white-pink flowers. It grows to about 60 cm (2 feet) and likes well drained sandy soil with a high iron content. In the right conditions the plant can be an invasive weed.

The plant yields very little essential oil, so is one of the most expensive on the market and widely adulterated. Because of this we use the hydrosol instead of the essential oil.

Lemon balm has an illustrious past and is often mentioned by traditional medics, it was described by John Evelyn (1620 -1706) as "sovereign for the brain, strengthening the memory, and powerfully chasing away melancholy". Melissa means honey bee in Greek, because they love the nectar of this herb.

Lemon balm is a strong anti-viral and immune stimulant. It is also used as a nerve sedative, digestive aid, antidepressant, and to regulate hormonal cycles. Lemon balm is tonic to the heart, slowing the heartbeat, and reducing blood pressure. We use it mainly for its powerful immune stimulant properties and for calming nerves, as it is relaxing without being sedative. This hydrosol strengthens ones sense of self, and is particularly suited to cats who are over-sensitive, or suffering from anxiety, especially in older cats.

Principle uses

Physical
- Dementia
- Immune stimulant
- Calming nerves, relaxing without being sedative

- Digestive aid, use in moderation
- FIV
- Mental function support
- Nerve damage
- Viral infection

Behavioural
- Hyperactivity
- Confused
- Lack of focus
- Nervous
- Depression

Frequently used for:

- Cats who appear shut down, withdrawn or over-excited and hyperactive especially if they are immune compromised.
- Friction in multi-cat households.
- Old cats.

Use as: Hydrosol, Herb fresh or dry

Cultivation/Sustainability: No known concerns.

Actions: Antiviral, antifungal, antidiabetic.

Safety & Cautions: Don't use in cases of hypotension, or glaucoma.

NEEM

(Azadirachta indica)

History and Character

The neem tree is known in India as "the village pharmacy". For more than 4,500 years traditional healers have used its bark, seeds, leaves, fruit, gum and oils for dozens of internal and external medical treatments. The most common historical uses of neem were for skin diseases, inflammation, fevers and as an antiparasitic.

In India it is claimed to be contraceptive. Neem oil is effective against at least 200 insects. It is apparently so distasteful that most of them won't eat a plant treated with it. But if they do, it throws their hormones into disarray, fatally preventing them from shedding their outgrown skins.

Principle uses

Physical

- Eczema
- Flea, tick and mosquito repellent
- Rheumatism and Arthritis
- Ringworm
- Scabies

Frequently used for:

- Insect repellent.
- Irritated skin, especially if accompanied by muscular skeletal stiffness.

Use as: Cold-pressed seed oil, Dried powder

Cultivation/Sustainability: No known concerns.

Nayana Morag and Julie-Anne Thorne

Actions: Analgesic, anthelmintic, antiviral, antibacterial, anti-fungal, anti-inflammatory, antiparasitic.

Safety & Cautions: Although the hormonal effect shown on insects has not been seen to affect mammals, do not use in pregnancy.

Neroli (Orange Blossom)

(Citrus aurantium, var. amara)

History and Character

The orange tree is a medium size flowering citrus, native to China, but now widely cultivated in any Mediterranean climate. It has glossy green, heart-shaped leaves, a smooth grey bark and masses of fragrant white flowers. Neroli is produced by steam distillation from the flowers of the tree. It is another costly essential oil that can easily be replaced with its hydrosol.

The oil is said to be named after an Italian princess who introduced the fragrance to Italian society in the 17th century. The fragrance is a classic floral note in perfumery. In the Middle East, orange blossom water is used for fainting fits and shock. Neroli has a powerful ability to reconnect body and mind after shock from emotional or physical trauma and is a 'must have' in the first aid kit.

Neroli is highly uplifting, calming, and steadies the nerves, (useful before vet visits, or other situations that provoke anxiety). Neroli heals sorrow held in the heart and eases the pain of loss or separation from a loved one.

Principle uses

Physical
- Gas or bloating
- Internally as a support for itchy skin caused by food intolerance
- Shock
- Steadies the heart physically and emotionally

Behavioural
- Before something stressful like traveling
- Heartbreak

Nayana Morag and Julie-Anne Thorne

- Loss
- Hysterical fear
- Sadness
- Separation
- Anxiety manifesting in the stomach

Frequently used for:

- Separation anxiety especially if there is a history of loss or bereavement the cat whimpers or cries.

Use as: Hydrosol, Essential oil

Cultivation/Sustainability: Cultivated, but often heavily sprayed with insecticides, use organic.

Actions: Antidepressant, anticoagulant, antiseptic, antispasmodic, aphrodisiac, carminative, digestive, nervine sedative and tonic.

Safety & Cautions: It is potentially drying to the skin. Don't use in cases of hypotension.

NETTLE
(Urtica dioica)

History and character

The familiar common nettle or stinging nettle is a herbaceous, perennial flowering plant in the family Urticaceae. The species is divided into six subspecies, five of which have hollow stinging hairs called trichomes on the leaves and stems. These are the bits that sting you! They grow 1-2 meters tall, growing throughout the spring and summer, then turn to seed and die off for the autumn and winter in colder climates. They prefer cool, shady spots.

Nettles are rich in nutrients such as magnesium, calcium, zinc, iron, selenium, potassium, vitamins A and C, and other trace minerals. They provide a great immune boost and are tonic to the body. We use the soft green leaves dried or as a macerated oil which is really nutrient dense.

Principal uses

Physical
- Allergies
- Kidney and urinary function
- Liver support
- Immune boost
- Arthritis
- Stimulates circulation
- Blood tonic
- Digestive support
- Anaemia
- Itchy skin

Nayana Morag and Julie-Anne Thorne

Frequently used for:

- Cats that are run down or recovering from an operation/anaesthetic. Particularly if they have kidney or liver problems and their coat is poor.

Use as: Dried leaf, Dried powder, Macerated oil

Cultivation/Sustainability: No known concerns. Use high quality, untreated dried products.

Actions: Antianemic, alterative, antiseptic, anti-inflammatory, detoxifying, diuretic, fortifying, hepatic, immune tonic, immunostimulant, kidney tonic, regenerative, restorative, soothing, stomachic.

Safety & Cautions: None known.

PEPPERMINT
(Mentha piperita)

History and Character

A perennial herb up to 1m/3 ft high with strong underground runners, green stems and leaves. There is also a black peppermint which has dark green serrated leaves and purplish stems. Peppermint has a long history of medicinal and culinary use. The essential oil is classified as a medicine for digestive problems, such as colitis and irritable bowel syndrome.

Energetically, peppermint is invigorating and awakening, bringing things into focus mentally and emotionally. It helps cats to be clear about their boundaries, so it is easy to take in and give out without defensiveness and with discrimination.

Principle uses

Physical
- Colitis
- Flatulence
- Heat stroke
- Indigestion
- Inflamed soft tissue
- Irritable bowel syndrome
- Nausea
- Loss of appetite
- Digestive stimulant

Behavioural
- Defensive of personal space
- Hyperactivity
- Irritability

Nayana Morag and Julie-Anne Thorne

- Lethargy
- Lack of focus

Frequently used for:

- Cats who have digestive issues or upsets, especially if they are defensive of their personal space.
- Cats who lack focus or are unable to settle.

Use as: Dried leaf, Hydrosol, Essential Oil

Cultivation/Sustainability: Cultivated.

Actions: Analgesic, anti-infectious, anti-inflammatory, anti-lactogenic, antispasmodic, antiviral, carminative, decongestant, digestive, expectorant, hepatic stimulant, hormone-like (ovarian stimulant), hypertensor, mucolytic, neurotonic, uterotonic.

Safety & Cautions: Peppermint essential oil is very potent, so we advise you use the herb or hydrosol. If you do offer the essential oil heavily dilute.

Rose

(Rosa damascena)

History and Character

Rose essential oil and hydrosol mostly comes from the Damask Rose, a bush rose up to 2 m/6 ft high with highly fragrant, pink, 36-petalled blooms. Originally a product of the orient, roses are now cherished all over the world, however the best oil is produced in Bulgaria and some parts of Turkey. The dried buds we use are from *Rosa centifolia*.

'The queen of flowers', dedicated to Aphrodite, rose is one of the most feminine aromatics and its cooling properties are second to none. It releases energy blocked because of emotional wounds, especially when this manifests as resentfulness and an attitude of, "I will reject you before you can reject me". It promotes self-love and allows the heart to be receptive, restoring trust in oneself and others. It also has a powerful effect on the hormonal system and balances the physical and emotional body.

This is another case where the essential oil is expensive, and the hydrosol just as effective, if not more so. The small dried rose buds are a great addition to a herb garden, helping cats relax and find their playful side.

Principle uses

Physical
- Astringent and cooling for the skin
- Eye wash to soothe redness and irritation
- Hormone balancer
- Post-natal recovery

Behavioural

- Loss of trust
- Resentful anger
- Self-abuse
- Those whose hearts have closed due to poor treatment
- Rejection
- Repressed emotions
- Hurt/sadness

Frequently used for:

- After spaying.
- Cats that have been abused, suffered sadness or loss, especially if they are resentful or angry.

Use as: Dried rose buds, Hydrosol

Cultivation/Sustainability: Cultivated, but heavily sprayed. Use organic.

Actions: Antidepressant, antiphlogistic, antiseptic, antispasmodic, aphrodisiac, astringent, laxative, sedative, tonic for the heart, liver and uterus.

Safety & Cautions: Don't use during pregnancy, except after labor has started.

Rosemary
(Rosmarinus officinalis)

History and Character

A strongly aromatic evergreen shrub up to 2 m/6 ft. tall, Rosemary is native to the Mediterranean. But it is widely cultivated as a culinary herb. It has an affinity to the head, stimulating the brain and encouraging hair growth. The old saying "Rosemary for remembrance" derives from its ability to enhance concentration and brain activity. But also, because it was burnt at the funerals of Greeks and Romans.

In the Middle Ages in France, rosemary was burnt to disinfect the air in hospitals. Since it was reputed to strengthen body and brain, it was also used as a general panacea. Energetically, rosemary is a very stimulating herb, but also strongly earthed and with a "can do" attitude. It boosts confidence and courage in those suffering from extreme self-doubt and helps mind and body function in harmony.

Principal Uses

Physical
- Hair loss or patchy coats
- Joint disease
- Muscular pain
- Respiratory congestion
- Sluggish circulation

Behavioural
- Disconnected emotionally or mentally
- Lack of confidence
- Nervous cats
- "All over the place"

Nayana Morag and Julie-Anne Thorne

Frequently used for:

- Nervous cats with thin coats or hair loss, who lack confidence and move stiffly.

Use as: Fresh herb, Hydrosol

Cultivation/Sustainability: No known concerns.

Actions: Analgesic, antibacterial, antifungal, anti-inflammatory, antiseptic, antispasmodic, antitussive, antiviral, cardiotonic, carminative, choleretic, cicatrizant, detoxicant, digestive, diuretic, emmenagogic, enuresis, hyperglycemic, hypertensor, hypotensive, litholytic, lowers cholesterol, mucolytic, neuromuscular, neurotonic, sexual tonic, stimulant (adrenal cortex), venous decongestant.

Safety & Cautions: Generally held to be non-toxic, non-irritant and non-sensitizing. Use in high dilution.

St John's Wort
(Hypericum perforatum)

History and Character

Hypericum macerated oil is an amazing blood-red color due to the presence of hypericin, an effective antiviral agent. It is made by macerating the buds and flowers picked at noon in mid-summer. In times gone by this plant was thought to protect against evil spirits, something often said of plants now known to have a strong psychological effect. St John's Wort is often used as a natural substitute for Prozac. Medieval Knights used it on sword wounds. It is now scientifically proven to be antibacterial and beneficial to wounds where there is nerve damage.

St John's Wort is indicated whenever there is nerve damage. It is also a great winter tonic, uplifting spirits in dark times. It is antidepressant. It is also anti-inflammatory and often selected by cats who suffer from arthritis, especially when its aggravated by cold weather. It's also a remedy for burns, including sunburn.

Principle uses

Physical
- Arthritis
- Bruises
- Burns
- Inflamed nerve conditions, such as sciatica
- Skin inflammations
- Wounds
- Viral infections
- Fits/seizures

Nayana Morag and Julie-Anne Thorne

Behavioural
- Unpredictable moods
- Depression
- Pain relief
- Extreme nervousness
- Stress/anxiety
- Worry

Frequently used for:

- Cats suffering with pain, arthritis or joint mobility issues, especially if they are depressive or detached.
- Older cats.

Use as: Dried leaf, Hydrosol, Macerated oil

Cultivation/Sustainability: No known concerns.

Actions: Analgesic, antibacterial, antidepressant, antifungal, anti-inflammatory, antimicrobial, antispasmodic, antiseptic, antiviral, astringent, diuretic, nervine, vulnerary.

Safety & Cautions: Ingestion of high doses of hypericum can cause photo-sensitization in light skinned cats. Do not use with other medications.

Sunflower Oil
(Helianthus anuus)

History and Character

Sunflower oil is the ideal choice for a neutral carrier oil, as it is essentially odourless. Since there is so much commercial production of sunflower oil it is really important to buy organic cold-pressed oil. If we were only allowed to have one carrier oil, this would be it.

Principal uses

Physical
- Bruises
- Rhinitis and sinusitis
- Skin ulcers
- Constipation

Frequently used for:
- This is a great carrier oil, so you can add barley grass or spirulina to it. Cats don't usually select the oil on its own.

Use as: Fixed oil

Cultivation/Sustainability: Cultivated, often GMO. Use organic. Do not use supermarket grade oil.

Actions: Anti-inflammatory, antibacterial, emollient, nutritive.

Safety & Cautions: Sunflower oil may cause an allergic reaction in people who are sensitive to the Asteraceae/Compositae plant family.

Nayana Morag and Julie-Anne Thorne

TEA TREE
(Melaleuca alternifolia)

History and character

Tea tree is a low growing tree with needle-like leaves and small yellow or purplish flowers. Native to Australia, the Aboriginal people used its leaves in a tea for fevers, colds, and headaches. It has been extensively researched in recent years and found to be a powerful immunostimulant and active against bacteria, fungi and viruses. Energetically, it is tremendously cleansing, fortifying the lungs and giving confidence. It is useful for those who feel victimized or unable to cope with worldly matters.

Despite its popularity in cat shampoos and the like, tea tree essential oil can be dangerous to cats. For this reason, we only use the hydrosol. It is an effective wound wash. It is also a good hydrosol to make available in water when there is a virus going around.

Principle uses

Physical
- Wound disinfectant
- Skin infections
- Boils
- Abscesses
- Immune stimulant
- Fever
- Viral infections

Behavioural
- Confusion about boundaries
- Self-protective

Frequently used for:

- As a wound wash or immune stimulant, especially if viral infection is suspected.

Use as: Hydrosol. Do not use the essential oil.

Cultivation/Sustainability: Cultivated. Prefer organic. Australia produces the best quality.

Actions: Antibacterial, antifungal, antiviral, anti-infectious, immunostimulant, expectorant, febrifuge and antiparasitic.

Safety & Cautions: Over use of essential oil has caused toxic shock in cats.

THYME

(Thymus vulgaris)

History and Character

Thyme is a small, evergreen shrub with tiny fragrant leaves and woody stems and is native to the hot, rocky slopes of the Mediterranean but is cultivated throughout the world. It was used by the Egyptians for embalming and by the Greeks to clean the air of infection because of its antibacterial nature. It has been widely used as a cooking herb, especially to preserve meat, testament to its antibacterial properties.

In Western herbal lore, thyme has been used for respiratory infections and digestive problems. Energetically, thyme is very warm and dry, especially the thymol chemotype, inspiring yang energy to flow smoothly. Thyme infuses the Kidney meridian with warmth, stimulating us at an essential level to overcome fear. This is supported by thyme's stimulant action on the lungs, which encourages deep, regular breathing. We call it the Brave Oil.

Principal Uses

Physical
- Respiratory problems, excess mucous
- Digestive disease and diarrhoea
- Circulatory stagnation
- Bacterial infections

Behavioural
- Lethargy
- Despondency
- Cats who lack courage

Frequently used for:

- Fearful cats who feel overwhelmed by life.
- Defensive aggression, especially if there is a tendency to produce excess mucous or diarrhoea.

Use as: Dry/fresh herb, Hydrosol

Cultivation/Sustainability: Cultivated or wild-crafted. No known concerns.

Actions: Antibacterial, antifungal, anthelmintic, antiseptic, antispasmodic, antitoxic, carminative, diuretic, expectorant, hypertensive, rubefacient, stimulant and vermifuge.

Safety & Cautions: It is contraindicated with high blood pressure. Thyme linalool is gentler and safer for cats if you can find it. Do not use the essential oil with cats.

VALERIAN ROOT
(Valeriana officinalis)

History and Character

A perennial herb growing to 1.5 metres/5 ft tall, with a hollow stem, deeply dissected leaves and masses of purple/pink flowers. The roots are short and thick and mostly show above ground. There are many species of valerian around the world and it has been used for conditions such as nervous tension, backache, intestinal colic. Its mediaeval name was 'All Heal'. It is a painkiller and a powerful sedative.

Valerian is one of the most stabilising of aromatics and can be used when the mind is overcome by emotion, leading to panic, hysteria or frozen fear. It slows the world down so the situation does not seem to be so overwhelming. We often use it when all the stress circuits are 'blown', resulting in extremes of fearful or aggressive behaviour.

Principal Uses

Physical
- Shock
- Sedation
- Cystitis
- Seizures
- Muscle relaxant

Behavioural
- Chronic fear
- Fear of known things
- Hysteria
- Panic
- Pathological insecurity
- Anxiety

- Overgrooming
- Stress

Frequently used for:

- Cats who become hysterical when fearful, especially of known things, or if their adrenal system has been overloaded.
- Cats who are nervous, worried and anxious.

Use as: Dried root, Dried powder, Hydrosol

Cultivation/Sustainability: Mostly wild-crafted. No sustainability issues.

Actions: Anodyne, antispasmodic, carminative, diuretic, hypotensive, regulator, sedative, stomachic.

Safety & Cautions: Non-toxic and non-irritant however some sensitisation has been reported in humans. It has a strongly sedating effect use in moderation and well diluted.

VETIVER
(Vetiveria zizanoides)

History and Character

A tall tropical grass with scented tufts and a spreading root system, vetiver is native to Southern India (where it is known as the Oil of Tranquility), Indonesia and Sri Lanka. It is, however, currently mostly cultivated in Java, Haiti and Réunion. Traditionally, Indians have used vetiver as a vermin repellent weaving the grass into aromatic matting for their houses.

The Indians anoint themselves with the oil in the hot season to help keep them cool, and in Ayurvedic medicine it is used for joint problems and eczema. Energetically, vetiver is the "Earth mother" oil, nurturing, calming and reassuring. It brings us back to the present and helps to gather scattered energies and get grounded.

Principal Uses

Physical
- Anemia
- Physically run down
- Underweight for no good reason
- Sexual excitability

Behavioural
- Emotional insecurity
- Perfectionists
- Pushy cats who try to control you/over dominant behaviours
- Restlessness
- Ungrounded cats who don't know where they begin and end
- Aggressive and anxious cats

Frequently used for:

- Cats who walk all over you in enthusiasm or fear, or don't know where their feet are, tend to knock things over, or step on you, and seek constant reassurance.
- Cats who are thin despite eating well and need nourishment, especially if they are anxious or withdrawn.

Use as: Hydrosol, Essential oil

Cultivation/Sustainability: Grows easily in tropical and temperate climates, used for soil and water conservation.

Actions: Antianaemic, antiseptic, circulatory tonic, emmenagogue, glandular tonic (pancreatic secretion), immunostimulant.

Safety & Cautions: Generally held to be non-toxic, non-irritant and non-sensitizing.

Violet Leaf
(Viola odorata)

History and Character

A low growing, spreading perennial with dark green heart-shaped leaves, violet flowers and a tuberous root. Violet leaf is native to Europe and can be found growing in shady protected areas. It was cultivated as far back as 400BC by the Greeks and has a long history of use as a medicine, mostly for congestive heart conditions and capillary fragility of the skin. British herbalists use both flower and leaf for eczema and skin eruptions, particularly when associated with rheumatic symptoms. Energetically, violet leaf is grounding and settling, giving the strength of heart to move on from situations where energy is caught in a pattern of mistrust.

Principal Uses

Physical
- Old cats with aches and pains and a loss of self confidence
- Chronic pain
- Arthritis

Behavioural
- Loss of trust in themselves or others
- New home/change of environment
- Nervous cats
- Closed down emotionally
- Fear of loud noises

Frequently used for:

- Insecure cats who try to hide their insecurity through 'loud' behaviour or when a change in environment or a traumatic incident has caused a change in behaviour.
- Change of home.
- Older cats in chronic pain, suffering silently.
- Cats that are scared by loud noises such as fireworks.

Use as: Essential oil (absolute)

Cultivation/Sustainability: Cultivated. No known issues.

Actions: Analgesic (mild), anti-inflammatory, antirheumatic, antiseptic, decongestant (liver), diuretic, expectorant, laxative, soporific, stimulant (circulatory).

Safety & Cautions: Generally held to be non-toxic, non-irritant and non-sensitising.

YARROW

(Achillea millefolium)

History and Character

Yarrow is a perennial herb growing up to 1 meter/3 ft. tall, but more usually less than half this height. It has a basal rosette of fern like leaves and a tall stem bearing a tight knit cluster of white to pale pink flowers that look like a shield. Protection is one of its signatures. Native to Eurasia and found in hedgerows throughout Britain, it has naturalized in most temperate zones.

Yarrow was reputed to have been used by Achilles (hence the name) for wounds caused by iron weapons. The stalks are traditionally used for reading the *I-Ching*. Yarrow helps release energy held around physical and emotional scars. In short, it helps clear past traumas, especially when they manifest as a combination of anger and fear. Yarrow is often selected by 'rescue' cats. The herb is a digestive tonic as well.

Principal Uses

Physical
- Allergies
- Arthritis
- Ear infections
- Inflammation
- Scars
- Skin problems of all kinds
- Sprains and strains
- Urinary infections
- Wounds

Behavioural
- Emotional release
- Fearful anger
- Past abuse
- Trauma
- Withdrawn

Frequently used for:
- Cats whose past history is unknown, especially if they are showing behavioural problems, or if there is a history of physical or emotional traumas.
- First aid to stop bleeding.
- As an anti-inflammatory.

Use as: Dry/fresh flowers, Hydrosol, Essential oil

Cultivation/Sustainability: No known concerns.

Actions: Anti-allergenic, anti-inflammatory, antiseptic, anti-spasmodic, carminative, expectorant, febrifuge, hemostatic, hypotensive.

Safety & Cautions: Generally held to be non-toxic, non-irritant and non-sensitizing. Avoid in pregnancy. Yarrow can occasionally trigger "acting out" of a past trauma when used for the first time.

YLANG-YLANG
(Cananga odorata)

History and Character

Ylang-ylang is a tall tropical tree with large shiny leaves and fragrant tender flowers, which can be pink or yellow. The yellow flowers are considered best for essential oil. Ylang-ylang is native to tropical Asia, but the major oil producers are in Madagascar, Réunion and the Comoro Islands.

In Indonesia the flowers are spread on the bed of newlyweds. It has also been used to encourage hair growth, combat fever (including malaria) and fight infections. Energetically, it is a deeply calming oil, slowing heart rate and breathing and helping in situations where emotions overwhelm reason. It boosts self-confidence and is great for young cats who are having hierarchy issues, or excessive sex drive.

Principal Uses

Physical
- Tachycardia
- Hypopnea
- Hair growth

Behavioural
- Sexual anxiety
- Stereotypical behaviour (over-grooming, pica etc)
- Young cats lacking self confidence
- Male dominant behaviour

Frequently used for:

- Young cats who are nervous, restless, or lack confidence, especially if there is hair loss.
- Cats who are bullying others in the household – it helps to comfort and reassure.

Use as: Essential oil

Cultivation/Sustainability: No known concerns.

Actions: Antidepressant, antiseptic, aphrodisiac, euphoric, hypotensive, sedative and tonic.

Safety & Cautions: Generally held to be non-toxic, non-irritant and non-sensitizing.

CLAYS AND POWDERS

CLAY

Clay (mud) is a powerful healing agent and aids the body's healing processes. In the wild, animals use clay and mud for detoxification, as a cure for itchy skin, and to protect themselves from insect bites. Clay can be used where skin needs soothing or tightening; for oozing or weepy skin; and to draw out abscesses. Clay creates a physical barrier against fleas, midges and fungi, and in the case of fungi dries out the moisture they thrive on. Add a teaspoon of clay to 100 ml of water to provide a source of natural minerals, to neutralise toxins and possibly control worms.

The colour of clay

There are several types of clay, each one having a different mineral content, absorptive quality and preferred use.

The clays we use most often for cats are French Green clay and Kaolin white clay. See Botanical Profiles for more info.

Green clay is strongly detoxifying and drawing, best for abscesses and for internal use. Also known as sea clay or Illite, French green clay contains high amounts of mineral including mineral oxides, magnesium, calcium, potassium, dolomite, silica, manganese, phosphorous, silicon, copper, and selenium. It also contains iron oxides and decomposed plant matter, such as kelp and seaweed, which gives the clay its colour. The more green the colour, the more active the clay. The clay is highly absorptive and negatively charged, so bacteria and dead cells are drawn into the clay and out of the body.

Kaolin clay is a fine powdery clay, soothing for skin, skin stimulant, pH neutral. Traditionally it has been used for diarrhoea and skin care. Kaolin, or 'china clay' as it is commonly called, is a hydrated aluminum silicate crystalline mineral formed over many millions of years by the hydrothermal decomposition of granite rocks. White kaolin clay has a neutral pH, and a high consistency of silica dioxide. It is used in natural toothpastes for humans. It is not as absorptive as green clay, but dusted on lightly it can help soothe and condition skin.

Safety

Clay can disrupt magnets so people with pacemakers should not use it. Clay should not be used in conjunction with any conventional medicines without professional advice. Use clay that is intended for internal use and always make sure there is access to fresh water as well as clay water if you are leaving it down for your cat.

DIATOMACEOUS EARTH

Diatomaceous earth (DE) is a chalk-like white powder made from the fossilized remains of single-celled organisms (diatoms) found in dried out lakes and riverbeds. It is almost pure amorphous silica. Each tiny speck is highly abrasive. When insects pass through it the DE damages their exoskeleton leading to death. It is considered to be a safe, effective flea deterrent when applied topically. Some people also suggest it can be used to control internal parasites. Because of its high silica content, it can be helpful for some skin problems and joint health.

It is important to use food grade Diatomaceous earth, which is DE that has been mined from the ground, pulverized, but left otherwise untouched. This form of diatomaceous earth is approved by the FDA and is generally regarded as safe.

Cautions:

DE is a very fine powder that can cause mild lung irritation if inhaled excessively. If you have sensitive lungs or sinuses it is best to wear a mask when applying. Avoid contact with eyes. See the flea powder recipe for suggest use. It can also be drying to skin if overused.

SPIRULINA

Spirulina is a blue-green algae classified as a cyanobacteria, containing a number of nutrients and vitamins. Due to a risk of contaminants in wild spirulina it is usually cultivated, ensuring it is fit for human consumption. The algae is slowly dried to create the powder we all know and love. Spirulina has recently been hailed as a super food and has become very popular in health food stores around the world.

This dark green powder is a great remedy to have in your kit to support the day to day health and well-being of your cat as it provides trace-nutrients and is rich in protein. It can be offered to older, sick or run-down cats as it is nutrient dense and immune supportive. It also helps to improve brain function and reduce inflammation caused by allergies. You can offer spirulina as a dried powder, with a dribble of water, or a carrier oil. Some cats prefer it well-diluted, some like it neat. Let your cat select.

Barley Grass

Barley grass is the leaf of the barley plant, one of the worlds oldest crop resources. The tips of the grasses contain an exceptional amount of nutrients and minerals and are highly nourishing.

Barley grass powder is another remedy to offer when your cat is run down or lacking in nutrients. It also helps with anxiety and muscle function as it is a rich source of magnesium.

You can offer your cat barley grass powder in the same way as spirulina. Or you can grow the grass yourself from seed outside or inside in a pot. This has the added benefit of cleaning the digestive tract, purging hairballs, cleaning teeth, and being a readily available vitamin and mineral supply. Whether you use dried powder or fresh grass – barley grass is a great remedy for your cat.

Conclusion

Now you should be feeling empowered to make a start and offer your cats some aromatic botanicals. The following charts will help you make your shortlist to start with, and what would suit your cat. Allow your cat to lead the way and enjoy the new depth of relationship you will discover.

Essential Oil	Physical indicators	Emotional Indicators	Common Uses
Angelica root *Angelica archangelica*	Heart disturbances, sluggish digestion, loss of appetite, hepatitis, fungal infection, immune problems, shortness of breath.	Hysteria, "switched off", nervous, fearful, hyperactive.	For cats who reject healing, early trauma, fear, debilitation, multiple problems. Overgrooming.
Bergamot *Citrus bergamia*	Tumours and growths, warts, sarcoids, bacterial infection of lungs or urinary tract, hormone imbalance, viral infection.	Depression, mood swings.	Warts/Tumours, infections of lungs or genito-urinary tract, balancing emotions, post parturition.
Carrot seed *Daucus carota*	Poor skin/nails, underweight, heart problems, cuts and bruises, liver damage.	Despondent, sense of abandonment.	Malnutrition, skin and coat, slow healing wounds, abandonment, hemorrhage. Overgrooming.
Calendula *Calendula officinalis*	Dry cracked skin, fungal infections, slow healing wounds, digestive disruption – vomiting after eating.	Lack of confidence, no emotional connection or displays of affection, nervous, timid.	New environment, problems of multi-cat households. Good all-round healer. Fungal infections.
Catnip *Nepeta cataria*	Constipation, diarrhoea, reduced appetite, vomiting, excess swallowing, hairballs.	Anxious, fearful, nervous, closed down.	Digestion issues, stress, anxiety, highly strung cats.
Cedarwood Himalayan *Cedrus deodara*	Coughs with white mucous, skin infections, insect repellent, general tonic, kidney problems, poor circulation, hair loss.	Insecure, timid, ungrounded, fearful, reactive.	Lymphatic drainage, coughs, backache, oedema, genito-urinary, timidity. Overgrooming.
Chamomile, German *Matricaria recutita*	Insect bites, sores, soft tissue swelling, fungal infections.	Anxious behaviours, hiding, hissing, irritability. Lack of patience and tolerance of others.	Anxiety, inflammation, allergies. Overgrooming.
Chamomile, Roman *Anthemis nobilis*	Nervous stomach, irritable skin, red eyes, runny eyes.	High strung, nervous, tantrums.	Nervousness, skin problems, nervous upset stomach, angry outbursts, problems with children.

Essential Oil	Physical indicators	Emotional Indicators	Common Uses
Clary Sage *Salvia sclarea*	Tight muscles, respiratory distress, shortness of breath, dry skin, hormonal imbalance.	Fearful, over reactive, tense.	Asthma, muscle spasm, hormonal imbalance, tension, claustrophobia, fear.
Cistus *Cistus ladaniferus*	Damaged skin, itching, bruises, scars, circulation, immune modulator.	Detached, fearful, over-reactive, blocked emotions, wild.	Itchy skin, scar healing, emotional detachment, any skin condition.
Comfrey *Symphytum officinale*	Lack of movement, joint issues.	Anxious, sudden change in behaviour, withdrawn.	Older cats, recovering from an operation or accident. Reduces inflammation.
Fennel *Foeniculum vulgare var. dulce.*	Flatulence, fatty lumps, lack/excess of milk, indigestion, excess hormones, poisoning.	Worry, exaggerated concern about others, emotionally needy.	False pregnancy, lactation problems, stomach upset, fluid retention, lipomas, flatulence, obesity.
Frankincense *Boswellia carterii*	Shortness of breath, nervous digestive upsets, dry, flaky skin, scars, growths.	Nervous fear, specific fears.	Fireworks, diarrhoea, asthma, lice, nervous cough, break with past, tumours, skin repair.
Geranium *Pelargonium graveolens*	Hormonal imbalance, dandruff, endocrine imbalance, sluggish liver/ kidneys.	Mood swings, overwhelmed insecure.	Hormonal problems, insecurity, new home, flaky skin, lice.
Ginger *Zingiber officinale*	Arthritis, cold sensitive, muscle stiffness, sore back, lung congestion, digestive.	Depression, self-protective, overwhelmed by life, no self-confidence.	Sluggish digestion/ circulation, travel sickness, weakness, stiff joints, old cats, lack of willpower.
Helichrysum *Helichrysum italicum*	Traumatic injury, allergies, run down, multiple problems, congestion, bruising, tendon injuries.	Deep emotional wounds, resentment.	Bruises, damaged tissue, past trauma, allergies.
Hemp *Cannabis sativa*	Slow, limited, reduced mobility. Arthritis, degenerative diseases. Dry skin, eczema, digestive issues.	Anxiety, nervousness, manic behaviours. Hypersensitive.	Anxious cats in a new environment, multi-cat households, rescue cats. Older cats.
Hops *Humulus lupulus*	Neutered cats, sexual mature male cats.	Bullying, aggressive, bold hyper-active.	Lowers testosterone. Particularly effective in male dominant multi-cat homes.

Essential Oil	Physical indicators	Emotional Indicators	Common Uses
Juniper berry *Juniperis communis*	Arthritis, muscle strain, soft tissue damage, weak kidneys, sluggish systems.	Disturbed mind, unsettled, aloof, gloomy, worried about themselves.	Arthritis, after hard work, post-op, soft tissue damage, liver congestion, clearing mind, psychic protection.
Lavender *Lavandula angustifolia*	Accidents, sensitive skin, heart palpitations.	Restless anxiety, mood swings, nervousness, shyness.	Wounds, burns, proud flesh, hot spots, skin damage, scars, hysteria, nervousness.
Lemongrass *Cymbopogon citratus*	Compromised immune system, growths, muscle pain, arthritis.	Emotionally needy, unfocused, insecure, worried.	Fly/flea repellent, tumours, depression, confusion, pain.
Linden blossom *Tilia cordata*	Sedative.	Cowering, hiding, hissing, fear, dis-trust, reactive, restless.	Helps to build trust and release blocked emotion around abuse or trauma. Overgrooming.
Lemon Balm *Melissa officinalis*	Immune stimulant, digestive aid, nerve damage, twitching limbs.	Hyperactivity, confused, lack of focus, depression, withdrawn.	Antiviral, antifungal, immune boost. Supports brain function and deterioration.
Neem *Azadirachta indica*	Arthritis, itchy skin, eczema, reactive to insects.	Irritable, restless.	Insect repellent, skin repair, flea allergy.
Neroli *Citrus aurantium*	Digestive disturbances, loss of appetite.	Anxious, depressed, lack of energy, lonely.	Cats who whimper or cry out. Loss, separation, bereavement.
Nettle *Urtica dioica*	Arthritis, dull coat, itchy skin, lack of appetite.	'Under the weather'.	Immune boost, liver tonic, kidney support.
Peppermint *Mentha x piperita*	Itchy skin, lack of appetite, constipation, shortness of breath, nerve damage, muscular strains, colic, burns.	Hyper-active, lack of energy or focus, space defensive.	Strains and sprains, digestive support, colitis, multi-cat households, damaged nerves.
Rose *Rosa damascena*	Anorexia, irritated eyes, hormone imbalance.	Anger, manic, resentful, sad, self-abuse, withdrawn.	After neutering, rescue cats, abused and angry, sadness. Overgrooming.
Rosemary *Rosmarinus officinalis*	Muscle pain, general sluggishness, clumsiness, hair loss.	Hard to connect with, aloof, yowling, confused.	Alopecia, convalescence, muscle strain, sinus/lung congestion, lack of concentration. Dementia.
St John's Wort *Hypericum perforatum*	Stiff, slow movement, seizures, fits, open wounds.	Anxiety, worry, retreating, shut down.	Old age, pain relief, depression, unpredictable moods.

Essential Oil	Physical indicators	Emotional Indicators	Common Uses
Tea Tree *Melaleuca alternifolia*	Sores, open wounds, boils, abscess, temperature.	Aloof, over-sensitive, self-protective.	Viral infections, wounds, irritated skin.
Thyme *Thymus vulgaris*	Respiratory issues, excess mucous, diarrhoea.	Fearful cats, over-whelmed. Lethargy, despondency.	Antibacterial, antifungal, antiseptic. Timid or fearful of others.
Valerian *Valeriana officinalis*	Shock, seizures, lack of urination, mobility issues, inappropriate urination in the home. Overgrooming.	Anxious movement, excess energy, fear, uncharacteristic aggression, withdrawn.	Shock, fearful or hysterical cats. Change of home, multi-cat households. Overgrooming.
Vetiver *Vetiveria zizanoides*	Under- or over-weight, general stiffness and discomfort, anemia.	Flighty, hyper-excitable, clumsy, knocks into you.	Hyper excitability, pushy, "no sense of their feet", weak constitution, debility.
Violet leaf *Viola odorata*	Lack of mobility, old age, stiffness.	Lack of trust in others, skittish in their environment, hiding away.	New home. After any destabilising incident. Stressful situations. Anxiety and worry. Chronic pain.
Yarrow *Achillea millefolium*	Injuries of all types, self-harm, allergies, irritated skin, liver or kidney congestion.	Past trauma, fearful anger, past abuse, unknown history.	Emotional/physical trauma, inflammation, itchy skin, wounds, allergies, insect bites.
Ylang-ylang *Cananga odorata*	High blood pressure, loss of libido, sensitive skin, hair loss.	Nervous, insecure, no self-confidence, no *joie de vivre*.	Young cats with hierarchy issues, dry skin, nervousness, hypernea.

Condition	Essential oil/ hydrosol/ powder	Carrier oil/ herbal oil	Dried herb
Musculo-skeletal problems, circulation, muscles, joints			
Aches and Pains	Carrot seed, cedarwood, chamomile, clary sage, ginger, helichrysum, spirulina, yarrow.	Calendula, comfrey, hemp, St John's Wort (SJW).	Chamomile, comfrey, SJW, nettle, valerian.
Arthritis	Angelica Root, carrot seed, cedarwood, fennel, ginger, juniper, spirulina, yarrow.	Comfrey, hemp, SJW.	Chamomile, comfrey, SJW, valerian.
Bruising	Chamomile, helichrysum, lavender.	Comfrey, calendula, sunflower.	Calendula, helichrysum, SJW, valerian.
Broken bones	Barley grass, helichrysum, lavender, yarrow.	Comfrey, SJW.	Comfrey, SJW.
Fluid Retention	Angelica root, cedarwood, chamomile, fennel, juniper.	Hemp, sunflower.	Chamomile, nettle.
Heart palpitations	Angelica root, chamomile, geranium, jasmine, neroli, rose, ylang-ylang.	Calendula, hemp, sunflower.	Angelica root, calendula, chamomile, lavender, rose.
Hypertension (high blood pressure)	Clary sage, lavender, neroli, ylang-ylang.	Calendula, hemp, sunflower.	Lavender.
Hypotension (low blood pressure)	Ginger, neroli, peppermint, rosemary, thyme.	Sunflower.	Peppermint.
Muscle cramps	Clary sage, juniper berry, spirulina, yarrow.	Calendula, hemp, sunflower.	Calendula, yarrow, valerian.
Muscle stiffness	Cedarwood, clary sage, ginger, juniper, spirulina, lemongrass.	Comfrey, hemp, SJW.	Catnip, comfrey, peppermint, SJW, valerian.
Neuro-muscular problems	Angelica root, roman chamomile, peppermint.	Calendula, SJW, sunflower.	Angelica root, calendula, valerian, chamomile, SJW.

Nayana Morag and Julie-Anne Thorne

Oedema	Angelica root, cedarwood, helichrysum, juniper, lemon, peppermint, rosemary, thyme.	Sunflower, calendula, comfrey.	Angelica root, calendula, comfrey, peppermint.

Problems of the Digestive System

Loss of appetite	Angelica Root, barley grass, bergamot, carrot seed, ginger, fennel, peppermint.	Hemp, sunflower.	Catnip, chickweed, nettle, peppermint.
Bloating	Barley grass, carrot seed, roman chamomile, fennel, peppermint.	Calendula, sunflower.	Chamomile, peppermint.
Colitis	Carrot seed, chamomile, peppermint.	Calendula, sunflower.	Chamomile, peppermint.
Constipation	Fennel, ginger, peppermint.	Sunflower.	Chickweed.
Diarrhoea	Roman chamomile, frankincense, ginger, neroli (chronic), thyme.	Calendula, nettle.	Chickweed, nettle, peppermint.
Digestive Disturbances	Angelica root, catnip, chamomile, fennel, frankincense, lemongrass, neroli, peppermint, thyme.	Calendula, chickweed, hemp, sunflower.	Catnip, chamomile, nettle, peppermint.
Flatulence	Bergamot, fennel, ginger.	Hemp, chickweed, sunflower.	Chickweed, peppermint.
Food Obsessed	Bergamot, carrot seed, fennel, rose.	Sunflower, nettle.	Nettle, rose.
Irritable Bowel Syndrome	Carrot seed, chamomile, peppermint.	Chickweed, hemp, sunflower.	Chamomile, chickweed, peppermint.
Liver tonic	Barley grass, carrot seed, geranium, ginger, helichrysum, juniper, lemon.	Calendula, nettle, sunflower.	Calendula, nettle.
Malnutrition (past and present),	Carrot seed, lemon, vetiver.	Hemp, sunflower.	Rose, jasmine, peppermint.
Nausea	Chamomile, ginger, peppermint.	Hemp, chickweed, sunflower.	Calendula, chamomile, chickweed, peppermint.
Obesity	Cedarwood, fennel.	Sunflower.	Chamomile, peppermint.

Pancreatic Problems	Angelica root, cedarwood, chamomile, cedarwood, fennel, ginger.	Calendula, comfrey.	Angelica root, calendula, chamomile, comfrey.
Sluggish Digestion	Barley grass, fennel, ginger, peppermint, thyme.	Hemp, sunflower.	Chickweed, peppermint.
Stress Related Digestive Problems	Angelica Root, chamomile, frankincense, neroli.	Chickweed, hemp, nettle, sunflower.	Angelica root, catnip, chamomile. Chickweed, nettle.
Worms	Bergamot, carrot seed, thyme.	Hemp, neem, sunflower.	
Ulcers	Angelica Root, carrot seed, frankincense, german chamomile.	Calendula, comfrey, sunflower.	Angelica root, chamomile, catnip, chickweed, peppermint.
Underweight	Angelica root, vetiver.	Hemp, sunflower.	Angelica root.

Problems of the Immune System

Allergies	Chamomile, fennel, helichrysum, hops, green clay, peppermint, yarrow.	Calendula, hemp, neem.	Calendula, chamomile, peppermint, yarrow.
Anaemia	Barley grass, carrot seed, roman chamomile, nettle, vetiver.	Hemp, nettle.	Chamomile, nettle.
Auto Immune Diseases	Angelica root, bergamot, carrot seed, chamomile, juniper berry, lemon balm, spirulina.	Hemp, SJW, sunflower.	Angelica root, chamomile, SJW.
Bacterial Infections	Bergamot, ginger, green clay, helichrysum, lemon balm, neem, tea tree, thyme.	Calendula, comfrey, SJW.	Calendula, comfrey, SJW.
Fever	Bergamot, valerian.	Calendula, sunflower.	Calendula, valerian.
Feline immunodeficiency virus (FIV)	Lemon Balm, spirulina.		
Immune Tonic	Angelica root, bergamot, chamomile, spirulina, vetiver.	Hemp, nettle, sunflower.	Angelica root, chamomile, nettle.
Parvo virus	Angelica Root, ginger, lavender, rosemary, thyme.	Hemp, SJW, sunflower.	Angelica root, lavender, SJW.

Lethargy	Cedarwood, peppermint, rosemary, spirulina, thyme.	Calendula, hemp, sunflower.	Calendula, peppermint.
Tumours	Bergamot, carrot seed, fennel, frankincense.	Comfrey, hemp, sunflower.	Comfrey.
Viral Infections	Bergamot, helichrysum, lavender, lemongrass, peppermint, rosemary.	Hemp, SJW, neem, sunflower.	Helichrysum, lavender.

Problems of the Nervous System

Nerve Damage	Peppermint.	SJW.	Helichrysum, peppermint, SJW.
Nerve Tonic	Angelica root, barley grass, catnip, cedarwood, clary sage, lemongrass, neroli, valerian.	SJW, sunflower.	Angelica root, catnip, SJW, valerian.
Nervous Exhaustion	Angelica root, catnip, chamomile (Roman), clary sage, helichrysum, lemon, vetiver.	Hemp, SJW, sunflower.	Angelica root, catnip, chamomile, hops, SJW.
Epilepsy	Clary sage, frankincense, lavender, rosemary, ylang-ylang.	SJW, sunflower.	Lavender, SJW, valerian.

Problems of the Reproductive & Endocrine System

Addison's disease	Angelica root, frankincense, geranium, lemon, peppermint.	Hemp, sunflower.	Angelica root, peppermint.
Irregular cycle	Chamomile, fennel, geranium, rose, yarrow.	Hemp, SJW, sunflower.	Chamomile, hops, rose, SJW, yarrow.
Genital infections	Bergamot, chamomile, lavender.	Calendula, SJW.	Calendula, chamomile, lavender, SJW.
Hormonal Problems	Bergamot, chamomile, clary sage, geranium, fennel, rose, valerian, yarrow.	Hemp, SJW, sunflower.	Chamomile, hops, rose, SJW, valerian, yarrow.
Hyperthyroidism	Spirulina, geranium, valerian.		Valerian.
Hypothyroidism	Geranium.	Sunflower.	
Insufficient milk	Fennel.	Comfrey, SJW.	Comfrey, SJW.
Metabolic Syndrome	Angelica root, bergamot, carrot seed, geranium, peppermint.	Hemp, SJW, sunflower.	Angelica root, peppermint, SJW.

Phantom Pregnancy	Clary Sage, fennel, geranium, peppermint, rose, vetiver, yarrow.	Calendula, SJW, sunflower.	Calendula, rose, peppermint, SJW, yarrow.
Post Parturition	Bergamot, chamomile, fennel, rose, yarrow.	Calendula, sunflower.	Chamomile, rose, yarrow, calendula.
Uncomfortable heat/season	Clary sage, chamomile, yarrow, valerian.	Calendula, hemp, SJW.	Calendula, chamomile, hops, SJW, valerian, yarrow.

Problems of the Respiratory System

Airborne Bacteria (kills)	Bergamot, thyme.		
Allergies	German chamomile, helichrysum, yarrow.	Calendula, comfrey, hemp.	Calendula, chamomile, helichrysum, yarrow.
Asthma/wheezing	Cedarwood, clary sage, frankincense, helichrysum, peppermint.	Comfrey, hemp, sunflower.	Comfrey, helichrysum, peppermint.
Bronchitis	Angelica root, ginger, helichrysum, peppermint, thyme.	Comfrey, hemp, sunflower.	Angelica root, comfrey, peppermint.
Excess Mucous	Angelica root, cedarwood, peppermint, thyme.	Comfrey, hemp, sunflower.	Angelica root, comfrey, peppermint.
Infections (general respiratory)	Angelica root, thyme.	Comfrey, hemp, sunflower.	Angelica root, comfrey.
Influenza	Angelica root, ginger, lavender, lemon, rosemary, thyme.	Comfrey, hemp, sunflower.	Angelica root, comfrey, lavender.
Pneumonitis	Thyme.	Comfrey, sunflower.	Comfrey.
Recurrent Airway Obstruction (RAO, COPD)	Clary sage, frankincense, helichrysum, peppermint.	Comfrey, hemp, sunflower.	Comfrey, helichrysum, peppermint.
Sinus Problems	Ginger, lavender, peppermint, rosemary.	Calendula, hemp, sunflower.	Calendula, lavender, peppermint.

Problems of the skin (including nails)

Allergic Dermatitis	Bergamot, german chamomile, helichrysum.	Calendula, hemp, sunflower.	Calendula, chamomile, helichrysum, rose.

Alopecia (hair loss)	Carrot seed, cedarwood, chamomile, clary sage, rosemary, ylang-ylang.	Chickweed, hemp, sunflower.	Chamomile, chickweed.
Coat (poor)	Carrot seed, spirulina.	Chickweed, hemp, chickweed, nettle, sunflower.	Chickweed, nettle.
Dandruff	Bergamot, cedarwood, geranium, spirulina.	Calendula, chickweed, nettle, sunflower.	Calendula, chickweed, nettle.
Eczema	Chamomile, helichrysum, lavender, yarrow.	Calendula, hemp, neem, sunflower.	Calendula, chamomile, helichrysum, lavender, yarrow.
Fungal infections	Angelica root, calendula, cedarwood, clary sage, chamomile, fennel, geranium, helichrysum, lavender, lemongrass, rosemary.	Calendula, neem.	Angelica root, calendula, chamomile, helichrysum, lavender.
Flea/Fly Repellent	Cedarwood, geranium, lavender, lemongrass, peppermint, vetiver.	Neem, sunflower.	Lavender, peppermint.
Lick granulomas (Overgrooming)	Angelica root, barley grass, carrot seed, cedarwood, chamomile, jasmine, linden.	Calendula, chickweed, comfrey, SJW.	Angelica root, chamomile, calendula, comfrey, rose, SJW, yarrow.
Hot Spots (moist dermatitis, wet excema)	Cedarwood, chamomile, helichrysum, lavender, thyme, yarrow.	Calendula, sunflower.	Calendula, chamomile, helichrysum, yarrow.
Infections	Lavender, thyme.	Calendula, comfrey, neem.	Calendula, comfrey, lavender.
Insect Bites	Chamomile, helichrysum, lavender, yarrow.	Hemp, sunflower.	Chamomile, helichrysum, lavender, yarrow.
Lice	Geranium, lavender, lemongrass, rosemary.	Neem.	Lavender.
Mange	Bergamot, chamomile (German), helichrysum, lavender, thyme.	Calendula, neem.	Calendula, chamomile, helichrysum.
Mosquito	Geranium, lemongrass.	Calendula, neem.	Calendula.
Proud Flesh	Chamomile, helichrysum, lavender.	Calendula.	Calendula, chamomile, helichrysum, lavender.

Pyoderma	German chamomile, helichrysum, lavender, thyme, yarrow.	Calendula, comfrey, neem.	Calendula, chamomile, helichrysum, lavender, yarrow.
Ringworm	Bergamot, chamomile, helichrysum, lavender, thyme.	Calendula, neem.	Calendula, chamomile, helichrysum, lavender.
Scars	Frankincense, lavender, neroli, yarrow.	Calendula, comfrey, SJW.	Calendula, comfrey, lavender, SJW, yarrow.
Skin Problems	Carrot seed (poor condition), geranium (flaky, greasy), german chamomile (eruptive), lavender, (eruptive), (damp, oozing), roman chamomile (stress-related, itchy), yarrow.	Calendula, chickweed, comfrey, hemp, SJW.	Calendula, chamomile, chickweed, comfrey, hops, lavender, SJW, yarrow.
Soft Lumps	Angelica root, fennel, ginger, seaweed.	Comfrey, hemp.	Angelica root, comfrey.
Sweet Itch	Cedarwood, geranium, chamomile, frankincense, lavender, yarrow.	Calendula, hemp, neem, sunflower.	Calendula, chamomile, lavender, yarrow.
Thrush	Thyme.	Calendula, sunflower.	Calendula, peppermint.
Ticks	Lemongrass.	Neem.	
Tumours	Bergamot, fennel, frankincense, juniper, lavender, lemon, rose.	Comfrey, hemp.	Comfrey, lavender, rose.
Ulcers	Frankincense, tea tree.	Calendula, sunflower.	Calendula, chamomile, peppermint.
Urticaria	German chamomile, helichrysum, lavender, yarrow.	Calendula, comfrey, hemp.	Calendula, chamomile, comfrey, yarrow.
Warts	Bergamot, carrot seed, lavender, tea tree.	Calendula, sunflower.	Calendula, lavender.
Urinary System Problems			
Adrenal exhaustion	Angelica root, cedarwood, frankincense, geranium, lemon, vetiver.	Sunflower, SJW.	Angelica root, SJW.
Bladder Infections	Bergamot, carrot seed, fennel, lavender, thyme, yarrow.	Sunflower.	Lavender, yarrow.

Bladder/kidney Stones	Fennel, jasmine, juniper, lavender, lemon.	Sunflower.	Jasmine, lavender.
Inappropriate urination	Angelica root, bergamot, carrot seed, frankincense, lemon, neroli, valerian, yarrow, ylang-ylang.	SJW, sunflower.	Angelica root, SJW, valerian, yarrow.
Incontinence	Carrot seed, cedarwood, lemon, rose, yarrow.	Hemp.	Rose, yarrow.
Kidney Infections	Bergamot, cedarwood, chamomile, juniper, lemon, thyme, yarrow.	Hemp, SJW, sunflower.	Chamomile, SJW, yarrow.
Kidney Tonic	Angelica Root, bergamot, cedarwood, geranium, ginger, lemon, yarrow.	Hemp, sunflower.	Angelica root, yarrow.

Ears & Eyes *(Do not put essential oils inside ears and eyes, use hydrosols)*

Ear Infections	Chamomile, yarrow.		Chamomile, yarrow.
Runny Eyes	Chamomile, cornflower, rose, sandalwood.		Chamomile, rose.
Aural Plaque	Lavender, thyme.	Calendula, neem, sunflower.	Calendula, lavender.
Conjunctivitis	Chamomile, cornflower, rose.		Chamomile, rose.
Ear Mites	Chamomile, lavender, thyme.	Calendula, neem.	Calendula, chamomile, lavender.
Glaucoma	Carrot seed.	Hemp, sunflower.	

First aid

Abrasions	Helichrysum, lavender, yarrow.	Calendula, comfrey.	Helichrysum, lavender, yarrow.
Abscesses	Thyme.	Sunflower.	
Boils	Bergamot, chamomile, helichrysum, thyme.	Calendula.	Calendula, chamomile, helichrysum.
Broken Bones	Helichrysum, yarrow.	Comfrey	Comfrey, helichrysum, yarrow.
Bruises	Helichrysum, lavender.	Comfrey, sunflower.	Comfrey, helichrysum, lavender.
Burns	Helichrysum, lavender.	Calendula, SJW.	Calendula, helichrysum, lavender, SJW.
Cuts	Helichrysum, lavender, yarrow.	Calendula, sunflower.	Calendula, helichrysum, lavender, yarrow.

Shock/Hysteria	Jasmine, lavender, neroli, rose, valerian, ylang-ylang.		Jasmine, lavender, rose, valerian.
Sprains & strains	Chamomile, helichrysum, peppermint, rosemary, yarrow.	Calendula, comfrey.	Calendula, chamomile, comfrey, helichrysum, peppermint, yarrow.
Sunburn	Chamomile, helichrysum, lavender, peppermint.	Calendula, SJW.	Calendula, helichrysum, lavender, peppermint.
Poisonous Bites	Angelica root, fennel, thyme.	Calendula, sunflower.	Angelica root, calendula.

Behaviour/emotional

Abandonment	Angelica root, carrot seed, frankincense, helichrysum, linden, jasmine, rose.	*For behavioural problems use neutral base oils such as sunflower*	Angelica root, jasmine, helichrysum, linden, rose.
Abuse	Angelica root, bergamot, carrot seed, helichrysum, rose, yarrow.		Angelica root, helichrysum, rose.
Aggression	Bergamot, clary sage, hemp, hops, peppermint, thyme.		
Anger	Bergamot, roman chamomile, helichrysum, rose, valerian, yarrow.		Chamomile, rose, valerian, yarrow.
Anxiety	Chamomile, clary sage, frankincense, hemp, hops, rose, valerian.		Chamomile, hops, rose, valerian.
Boredom	Peppermint, rose, rosemary.		Peppermint, rose.
Bullying	Bergamot, hops, peppermint, rose, ylang-ylang.		Hops, peppermint, rose.
Claustrophobic	Clary sage, frankincense, lavender.		Lavender.
Companion (loss)	Frankincense, jasmine, linden, neroli, rose, yarrow.		Jasmine, linden, rose, yarrow.
Concentration (lack of)	Cedarwood, peppermint, rosemary.		Peppermint.
Confidence (lack of)	Calendula, cedarwood, ginger, rosemary, valerian, ylang-ylang.		Calendula, valerian.
Crowds (overwhelmed by/ restless in)	Angelica root, juniper berry, valerian.		Angelica, valerian.
Death	Frankincense, helichrysum, jasmine, neroli, rose.		Helichrysum, jasmine, rose.

Depressed	Bergamot, geranium, ginger, neroli, rose, SJW, thyme, valerian.	Rose buds, SJW, valerian.
Defensive aggression	Angelica root, clary sage, frankincense, linden, peppermint, rose, thyme.	Angelica root, linden, peppermint, rose.
Disengaged	Angelica root, juniper berry, rosemary, linden blossom, rose.	Angelica root, linden, rose.
Erratic Behaviour	Angelica root, bergamot, calendula, chamomile, clary sage, rose.	Angelica root, calendula, chamomile, rose.
Fear	Angelica root, cedarwood, chamomile, frankincense, hemp, linden, thyme, valerian, yarrow, ylang-ylang.	Angelica root, chamomile, linden, valerian, yarrow.
Flighty	Angelica root, cedarwood, chamomile, neroli, rose, valerian, vetiver.	Angelica root, chamomile, rose, valerian.
Frustration	Bergamot, chamomile, clary sage, hops, valerian.	Chamomile, hops, valerian.
Hierarchical Issues	Peppermint, rose, ylang-ylang.	Peppermint, rose.
Hyperactive	Catnip, chamomile, rosemary, vetiver, valerian.	Catnip, chamomile, valerian.
Impatient	Chamomile, clary sage, helichrysum.	Chamomile, helichrysum.
Insecure	Angelica root, calendula, catnip, fennel, geranium, ginger, rose.	Angelica root, calendula, catnip, rose.
Irritability	Bergamot, chamomile, helichrysum, peppermint.	Chamomile, helichrysum, peppermint.
Lethargic	Bergamot, calendula, cedarwood, ginger, peppermint, rosemary.	Calendula, peppermint.
Moodiness	Bergamot, calendula, clary sage, geranium, rose.	Calendula, rose.
Nervous	Angelica root, catnip, cedarwood, chamomile, clary sage, frankincense, geranium, lavender, vetiver, valerian, ylang-ylang.	Angelica root, catnip, lavender, valerian.
New home	Cedarwood, geranium, jasmine, rose, valerian.	Jasmine, rose, valerian.
Obsessive Behaviours:	Calendula, fennel, jasmine, rose, valerian.	Calendula, jasmine, rose, valerian.
Pushy	Angelica root, vetiver, ylang-ylang.	Angelica root.

Restless	Catnip, clary sage, frankincense, juniper berry, lavender, rose, valerian, vetiver, ylang-ylang.	Catnip, lavender, rose, valerian.
Self-Harm/Mutilation:	Angelica root, carrot seed, hemp, jasmine, rose, valerian.	Angelica root, jasmine, rose, valerian.
Separation Anxiety	Angelica root, cedarwood, chamomile, frankincense, hemp, neroli, ylang-ylang, valerian.	Angelica root, chamomile, valerian.
Shy	Cedarwood, ginger, lavender, thyme.	Lavender.
Suspicious	Juniper berry, valerian.	Valerian.
Timid	Cedarwood, lavender, thyme, vetiver.	Lavender.
Trauma	Angelica root, jasmine, rose, yarrow.	Angelica root, jasmine, rose, yarrow.
Travel Phobia	Frankincense, ginger, linden, neroli, peppermint.	Linden, peppermint.
Worry	Angelica root, fennel, frankincense, jasmine, peppermint.	Angelica root, jasmine, peppermint.

Nayana Morag and Julie-Anne Thorne

GLOSSARY OF TERMS

Amenorrhoea: Absence of menstruation

Anaemia: Deficiency in either quality or quantity of red blood corpuscles

Anesthetic: Substance causing loss of feeling or sensation

Analgesic: Relieves pain without producing anesthesia

Anaphrodisiac: Reduces sexual desire

Anodyne: Stills pain and quiets disturbed feelings

Antacid: Counteracts or neutralizes acidity (usually in the stomach)

Anthelmintic: Destroys intestinal worms

Antiallergenic: Relieves or controls allergic symptoms

Antianemic: Prevents or cures anaemia

Antianxiety: Prevents or cures anxiety

Antiarthritic: Prevents or cures arthritis

Antibacterial: destroys bacteria or inhibits their growth

Anticatarrhal: Relieves inflammation of the mucous membranes in the head and reduces the production of mucous

Anticoagulant: Prevents or stops the blood clotting

Anticonvulsant: Stops, prevents or lessons convulsions/seizures

Antidepressant: Prevents or cures depression

Antiemetic: Reduces nausea/vomiting

Antifungal: destroys or prevents the growth of fungi

Antihistamine: Used to treat allergies because it counteracts the effects of histamine such as swelling, congestion, sneezing and itchy eyes

Anti-inflammatory: Reduces inflammation

Antilactogenic: Reduces milk production

Antineuralgic: Relieves neuralgia (nerve pain), an acute, intermittent pain that radiates along a nerve

Antioxidant: Antioxidants are substances that prevent or slow oxidation to prevent cell damage

Antiparasitic: Kills or inactivates parasites

Antiphlogistic: Reduces inflammation

Antipruritic: Relieves itching

Antirheumatic: Relieves rheumatism

Antisclerotic: Prevents hardening of tissue

Antiseborrhea: Prevents the abnormal secretion and discharge: of sebum, which gives the skin an oily appearance and forms greasy scales

Antiseptic: Inhibits the growth and reproduction of microorganisms, when applied to the body they: reduce the possibility of infection, sepsis or: putrefaction

Antispasmodic: Prevents/eases spasms or convulsions

Antisudorific: Prevents or inhibits sweating/perspiration

Antitoxic: Counteracts a toxin or poison

Antitussive: Inhibits the cough reflex helping to stop coughing

Antiviral: Inhibits growth of a virus

Aperient: Mildly laxative

Aphrodisiac: Increases sexual desire

Arthritis: Inflammation of joints

Astringent: Causes contraction of organic tissues, control of bleeding, styptic

Bactericidal: Kills bacteria

Calmative: Mildly sedative, relaxing

Cardio-tonic: Strengthens and invigorates the heart

Carminative: Reduces flatulence, settles digestive system

Cephalic: Diseases affecting the head/remedy for disorders of the brain

Cholagogue: Stimulates secretion of flow of bile into duodenum

Choleretic: Stimulates the production of bile by the liver

Cicatrizant: Promotes formation of scar tissue, aids healing

Concrete: Waxy concentrated solid or semi-solid perfume material, prepared from live plant matter

Decongestant: Relieves congestion, usually by reducing the swelling of the mucous membranes in the nasal passages

Deodorant: Masks or suppresses odors

Detoxicant: Removes toxins - substances which have a harmful chemical nature

Digestive Stimulant: Stimulates digestion

Digestive Tonic: Strengthens and invigorates digestion

Diuretic: Aids production of flow of urine

Emmenagogue: Induces menstruation

Emollient: Softens, soothes and lubricates the skin

Energizing: Invigorates and gives energy

Enuresis: Urinary incontinence

Euphoric: Exaggerated feeling of well-being or elation

Expectorant: Promotes clearing of chest/lungs

Febrifuge: Combats fever, antipyretic

Fortifying: Strengthening

Glandular Tonic: Strengthens and invigorates the glands

Hemostatic: Stops bleeding

Hepatic: Any compound that acts on the liver

Hormone-like: Acts like a hormone

Hydrosol/hydrolat: Bi-product from essential oil distillation

Hyperglycemic: Having excessively high blood sugar

Hypoglycemic: Having excessively low blood sugar

Hypertensive: Raises blood pressure

Hypo-uricemic: Breaks down uric acid

Hypotensive: Lowers blood pressure

Immune Tonic: Strengthens and invigorates the immune system

Immunostimulant: Stimulates various functions or activities of the immune system

Infusion: Herbs etc. steeped in liquid to extract soluble: constituents

Insect Repellent: Repels insects

Insecticide: Kills insects

Kidney Tonic: Strengthens and invigorates the kidneys

Lactogenic: Enhances milk production

Laxative: Moves the bowels and aids digestion

Leucocyte-stimulant: Increases the production of leukocytes, white: blood cells, part of the immune system

Limbic system: A group of interconnected deep brain structures, common to all mammals, and involved in olfaction, emotion, motivation, behaviour, and: various autonomic functions

Litholytic: An agent that dissolves urinary calculi (stones)

Macerated oil: Infusion of herbs in vegetable oil

Mucolytic: Dissolves mucous

Nervine: Having a soothing effect on the nerves

Neurotonic: Strengthens and invigorates the nerves

Estrogen-Like: Has a similar effect on the body to that of estrogen

Olfactory system: The parts of the body involved in sensing smell, including the nose and many parts of the brain

Pancreatic-stimulant: Increases pancreatic activity

Parasiticide: Destroys parasites internally and externally

Pathogenic: Causing or producing disease

Pathological: Unnatural or destructive process on living tissue

Phlebotonic: Having a toning action on the veins

Purgative: Strongly laxative

Pyorrhea: Bleeding or discharge of pus

Regenerative: Restores or revives tissue growth

Reproductive stimulant: Increases reproductive activity in the body

Restorative: Restores health or strength

Rubefacient: Causes redness of skin, possibly irritation

Sedative: Reduces excitability and calms

Sexual Tonic: Strengthens and invigorates the sexual function

Nayana Morag and Julie-Anne Thorne

Smooth Muscle Relaxant: Relaxes the smooth muscles, which are muscles that contract without conscious control and are found in the walls of internal organs such as stomach, intestine and bladder

Soothing: Brings comfort or relief

Soporific: Sleep inducing

Stimulant: Increases physiological or nervous activity in the body, promotes activity, interest or enthusiasm

Stomachic: Promotes digestion or appetite

Styptic: Astringent, stops bleeding

Sudorific: Diaphoretic, produces sweat

Tincture: Alcoholic solution of some (usually vegetable) principle used in medicine

Tonic: Produces or restores normal vigor or tension: (tone)

Uterine Tonic: Strengthens and invigorates the uterus

Vasodilator: Widens or dilates blood vessels

Vermifuge: Expels intestinal worms, anthelmintic

Vesicant: Causes blistering to skin, a counter-irritant by external application

Vulnerary: Promotes healing of wounds

INDEX

A
Aggression 35, 52, 81, 103, 104, 114, 135, 154, 163, 164
Allergies 78, 99, 121, 142, 149, 151, 152, 154, 157, 159, 168
Angelica Root 35, 42, 52, 53, 54, 65, 67, 151, 155-165
Anxiety 15, 50, 51, 53, 54, 66, 68, 78, 79, 80, 82, 84, 92, 93, 101, 103, 105, 110-112, 115, 119, 120, 130, 136, 144, 150-154, 163, 165, 167
Arthritis 21, 24, 30, 66, 78, 82, 87, 91, 97, 101, 107, 111, 117, 121, 129, 130, 140, 142, 152, 153, 155, 167, 169
Asthma 76, 84, 93, 94, 99, 152, 159

B
Bacteria 31, 55, 56, 59, 61, 62, 67-69, 92, 96, 99, 110, 118, 128-135, 148, 151, 154, 157, 159, 167, 169
Barley Grass 131, 150, 155-158, 160
Bergamot 52-54, 64, 68, 69, 151, 156-164
Bruising 56, 152, 155
Bullying 105, 106, 145, 152, 163

C
Calendula 36, 50-53, 57, 60, 61, 63, 64, 72, 151, 155-164
Carrot Seed 27, 53, 54, 64, 70, 151, 155-158, 160-163, 165
Catnip 9, 12, 20, 22, 63, 74, 75, 151, 155-158, 164, 165

Cedarwood Himalayan 35, 52-54, 64, 76, 151, 155-165
Chamomile 15, 50, 51, 53, 54, 64, 78, 80, 151, 155-165
Chamomile, German 78, 80, 157, 159, 161
Chamomile, Roman 50, 51, 64, 78, 80, 155-157, 161, 163
Cistus 52, 86, 152
Clary Sage 53, 54, 84, 152, 155, 158-160, 163-165
Comfrey 15, 43, 54, 60, 89, 152, 155
Constipation 82, 91, 131, 151, 153, 156-163

D
Dandruff 34, 35, 96, 152, 160
Dental care 61
Depression 68, 71, 72, 85, 98, 112, 116, 130, 151-153, 168
Diarrhoea 80, 87, 93, 97, 98, 111, 134, 135, 148, 151, 152, 154, 156
Diatomaceous Earth 50, 148, 149

E
Ear wash 61

F
Fear 12, 14, 34, 35, 52, 66, 67, 76, 77, 80, 81, 84, 85, 87, 93, 94, 80, 114, 120, 134-137, 139, 140, 142, 143, 151-154, 164
Fennel 91, 152, 155-165
Feline immunodeficiency virus (FIV) 116, 157
First aid 55, 56, 119, 143, 162
Frankincense 52, 53, 64, 93, 152, 156-159, 161-165
Fungal 15, 55, 57, 67, 72, 78, 85, 92, 95, 96, 100, 110, 111, 116, 118, 128, 130, 133, 135, 151, 153, 154, 160, 168

G
Geranium 35, 51-53, 95, 152, 155, 156, 158-162, 164
Ginger 24, 54, 97, 152, 155-157, 159, 161-165
Glucurodination 12

H

Helichrysum 53-56, 60, 61, 99, 152, 155-164
Hemp 29, 35, 53, 54, 64, 101, 103, 152, 155-165
Hops 51, 52, 101, 103, 152, 157-159, 161, 163, 164

I

Insect 14, 26, 51, 76, 78, 96, 117, 118, 147, 148, 151, 153, 154, 160, 170
Insecure 92, 96, 106, 141, 151-154, 164
Irritable Bowel Syndrome (IBS) 16, 123, 156

J

Jasmine 40, 42, 52, 54, 105, 155, 156, 160, 162-165
Juniper Berry 107, 153, 155, 157, 163-165

L

Lavender 26, 27, 55, 56, 60, 61, 64, 109, 110, 153, 155, 157-165
Lemongrass 21, 51, 64, 111, 153, 155, 156, 158, 160, 161
Lemon Balm 54, 64, 115, 153, 157
Linden Blossom 432, 52, 54, 113, 153, 160, 163-165

M

Multi-cat households 17, 22, 24, 50, 53, 73, 75, 102, 104, 110, 116, 151-154

N

Neem 29, 50, 51, 62, 117, 153, 157, 158, 160-162
Neroli 25, 51, 52, 54, 55, 57, 64, 119, 153, 155-158, 161-165
Nervous 65, 66, 72, 80, 81, 87, 88, 99, 101, 103, 105, 106, 108, 110, 111, 114, 116, 127, 128, 130, 136, 137, 140, 145, 151-154, 158, 164
Nettle 20, 57, 121, 153, 155, 156, 157, 160
Noise 53, 93, 94, 140, 141

O
Overgrooming 54, 59, 66, 71, 77, 82, 106, 114, 137, 151, 153, 154, 160

P
Pain 15, 34, 39, 40, 43, 54, 55, 57, 66, 67, 82, 89, 97, 99, 111, 113, 119, 127, 130, 136, 140, 141, 153-155, 167, 168

Peppermint 14, 20, 22, 50, 53, 74, 123, 124, 153, 155, 156-161, 163-165

R
Rose 27, 28, 42, 52, 53, 63, 86, 125, 126, 153, 155, 156, 158-165
Rosemary 25, 127, 153, 155-160, 163, 164

S
Sadness 54, 120, 126, 153
Spirulina 54, 131, 149, 150, 155, 157, 158, 160
St John's Wort 54, 129, 153, 155, 157-164
Stress 9, 11, 15-17, 20, 21, 24, 50, 51, 53-56, 61, 66, 74, 80, 81, 106, 110, 119, 130, 136, 137, 151, 152, 154, 157, 161, 183
Sunflower Oil 27, 29, 30, 40, 42, 64, 131, 155-163

T
Tea Tree 12-14, 56, 60, 61, 132, 154, 157, 161
Thyme 61, 134, 135, 154-165
Thyroid 158
Ticks 50, 161
Trauma 43, 55, 56, 66, 67, 86, 87, 89, 119, 141-143, 151-154, 165

V
Valerian 15, 35, 43, 50-54, 57, 63, 101, 103, 136, 154, 155, 157-159, 162-165
Vetiver 30, 52, 64, 138, 154, 156-161, 164, 165
Violet Leaf 52, 53, 140, 154

W
Warts 68, 69, 151, 161
Worry 54, 55, 81, 91, 92, 130, 152-154, 165
Wounds 14, 55, 56, 70, 72, 87, 89, 90, 93, 99, 110, 125, 129, 142, 151-154, 172

Y
Yarrow 22, 54-56, 63, 64, 142, 143, 154, 155, 157-165
Ylang-ylang 54, 144, 154, 155, 158, 160, 162-165

Z
Zoopharmacognosy 11, 14, 180, 183, 185

RESOURCES

VIDEOS OF CATS INTERACTING WITH ESSENTIAL OILS

Cat selecting essential oils,
https://www.youtube.com/watch?v=hhq773D0KNI

Books

So many books, so little time, but here are a few we have enjoyed.

Aromatics

- Aromatherapy for Healing the Spirit, *Gabriel Mojay*
- Carrier Oils, *Len Price, with Ian Smith and Shirley Price*
- Hydrosols, The Next Aromatherapy, *Suzanne Catty*
- Medical Aromatherapy: Healing with Essential Oils, *Kurt Schnaubelt*
- The Complete Guide to Aromatherapy, *Salvatore Battaglia*
- The Encyclopedia of Essential Oils, *Julia Lawless*
- Understanding Hydrolats: The specific hydrosols for aromatherapy, *Len and Shirley Price*

Zoopharmacognosy

- Essential Oils for animals, *Nayana Morag*
- Wild Health, How animals keep themselves well and what we can learn from them, *Cindy Engel*
- How animals heal themselves, *Caroline Ingraham*
- You can heal your pet, *Elizabeth Whiter and Dr Rohini Satish MRCVS*

Cat health and behaviour

- Your Cat. Simple new secrets to a longer, stronger life *Elizabeth M. Hodgkins, D.V.M., Esq.*
- Natural Nutrition For Cats: The Ultimate Diet, *Kymythy Schultze*
- Four Paws Five Directions, *Cheryl Schwartz, DVM*

Aromatic Suppliers

There are many quality suppliers of aromatics, these are some we have sampled and like. It is not a comprehensive list. Just because someone is not on it does not mean their oils are not good, simply that we have not tried them.

USA

- Eden Botanicals
- Floracopeia
- Aromatics International
- Nature's Gift
- Stillpoint Aromatics

Europe

- Kobashi
- Materia Aromatica
- Florihana
- Oshadhi
- Over the Edge Farm
- Norfolk Essential oils
- Wild Health Shop
- My Animal Matters Ltd
- Naturally Cats

Nayana Morag and Julie-Anne Thorne

About Nayana

Nayana Morag grew up in the UK in a large family of humans and animals, the perfect environment for learning about animal behaviour. She was one of those kids with a natural empathy for animals, always gravitating towards the needy and vulnerable.

Nayana was introduced to Caroline Ingraham the pioneer of applied zoopharmacognosy in 1997 and from the first time she saw a horse select an essential oil she was hooked. Nayana earned her Certificate in Animal Aromatherapy and Touch for Health for Animals in 1999. She is also certified in Herbalism, Aromatherapy, Kinesiology, Aromatic Energetics and the 5 Elements, and Equine Acupressure.

Over the years, Nayana teaches her system of animal wellness that incorporates aromatics, Traditional Chinese Medicine, and reducing stress through management and diet. She calls her system Animal PsychAromatica and offers courses at all levels to students around the world. If you have any queries or comments about the book or would like to learn from Nayana, you can reach her through *www.essentialanimals.com*. You can also visit her farm in Portugal where she runs workshops in essential oils and natural animal care, distilling essential oils, and being with horses.

ABOUT JULIE-ANNE

Julie-Anne lives in the UK and has grown up with cats in her family. She was always drawn to cats wherever she went, and they instinctively sought her out. Julie-Anne was a quiet, introverted girl and not only found comfort with cats but felt like they understood her.

After getting a Psychology Degree she moved to Gloucester and rescued her very own cat, Pickle. Pickle was very poorly and led Julie-Anne to investigate, learn and train in alternative and complementary therapies, starting with Reiki level I and II.

She then expanded this knowledge with a diploma in Animal Healing with Elizabeth Whiter, the foundation and diploma in Feline Zoopharmacognosy with Caroline Ingraham and a diploma in Cat Care, Welfare and Behaviour. Bringing all of this together she created Naturally Cats. Holistic help for cats and their guardians.

These days Julie-Anne helps cats with a variety of problem behaviours using a mixture of environment enrichment, behaviour modification and botanical remedies. She connects with each cat on an emotional level and helps to give the cat a voice when she works with the family. She teaches the cats guardian how to see things from the cats perspective and becomes an interspecies interpreter.

Having been featured in Your Cat Magazine, Cat World Magazine and as a regular feature writer for the holistic cat magazine Edition Cat you can find out more about Julie-Anne's work here: *www.naturallycats.co.uk*

Lightning Source UK Ltd.
Milton Keynes UK
UKHW050425291220
375758UK00010B/114